Gardner Family
Back Row: Tanner, Nate, Cameron, Sean, Stella, Sara, Jason, Kona, Sage
Middle Row: Zach, Megan, Olivia, Sidney, Ashton, Sterling, Shelli, Jon, Seth, Phoebe, Shalae
Front Row: Shelby, Sam, Seth
Inset: Shanna

*To love what we do
and share what we love,
as we help others enjoy creativity
and worthwhile accomplishments
. . . in this we make a difference!*

statement of the heart

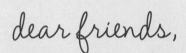

dear friends,

We're celebrating our return to an annual catalog with a fresh, vibrant redesign that I love—I hope you do too! The "swatches" showing our color families are fun and eye-catching, the pages separating each section show off several Designer Series paper artwork, the creative stitching draws your eye to valuable stamping and crafting tips, and the full-colored boxes that feature specific products used to create certain projects are helpful and informative.

Of course, those are all design elements that hopefully draw attention to what we're really all about—exclusive artwork, quality products, and inspiring ideas.

And I'm thrilled with what we're offering in those areas as well. We are committed to providing an impressive variety of images, styles, and greetings. You'll find everything from bold to intricate and line art to Two-Step. There's elegance, whimsy, contemporary, humor, and beauty—something for everyone!

I'm also excited about our collections—wonderful groupings of products that coordinate perfectly together in color and theme, making it even easier to quickly identify what you need to create your seasonal or special occasion projects.

Whether you enjoy cardmaking, scrapbooking, gift giving, or home décor, within the pages of this catalog you will find everything you need to explore and express your creativity—all without leaving the comfort of your own home!

Shelli

Shelli Gardner
Cofounder and CEO

1

table of contents

We make it easy to find everything you need to inspire, create, and share.

© STAMPIN' UP!

3

our stamps and products

Enjoy Stampin' Up!® artwork on coordinating stamp sets and other exclusively designed products. Because our sets are die cut, you can assemble them in seconds and start stamping right away! And don't miss our accessories, many of which are designed to coordinate with our stamp artwork. Use the products individually, or mix and match for greater impact.

Our images earned the 2009 *Creating Keepsakes* Readers' Choice Award for best rubber stamps—for the ninth year in a row! And our Idea Book & Catalog received the Reader's Choice Award for best idea book.

browse the collections

Throughout the catalog, you'll see that many of our products are featured in collections. Each collection includes products that coordinate in color, texture, and theme. Our collections make it easy to create coordinating, handcrafted keepsakes.

décor and more

Decorate your walls and create custom décor with our easy-to-apply vinyl elements. Use them to redecorate an entire room or to refresh select pieces such as frames and tiles.

shelli's signature ♡

This catalog also features Shelli's Signature Collection, products that Stampin' Up! cofounder and CEO Shelli Gardner loves because they reflect her personal style or make creativity more simple and fun. To see Shelli's product picks, look for stamp sets and accessories marked with a heart symbol. Then try them out to see what you can create!

about our stamps

The foam-backed rubber and deeply etched designs on each stamp ensure that your images remain sharp, resulting in exceptional projects. Our blocks are made of solid maple wood, with side grips that ensure ease of use. All stamp sets shown in this catalog are shown at 100% unless otherwise noted.

dress it up

Use our accessories to give your projects the finishing touch. Whatever look you want, you can achieve it with our coordinating ribbon, buttons, glitter, and more. Look for color coordinating accessories shown throughout the catalog.

color families

Stampin' Up! makes choosing color combinations easy! With our four color families, In Color® collection, and selection of neutral colors, you're sure to find coordinating shades you love for every project. And don't miss the accessories available in many of these exclusive colors.

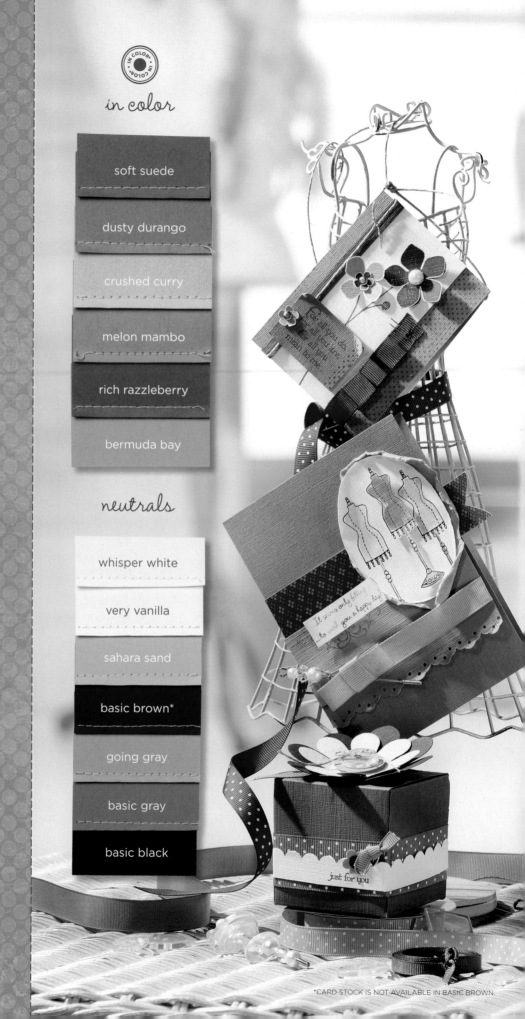

in color

soft suede

dusty durango

crushed curry

melon mambo

rich razzleberry

bermuda bay

neutrals

whisper white

very vanilla

sahara sand

basic brown*

going gray

basic gray

basic black

just for you

*CARD STOCK IS NOT AVAILABLE IN BASIC BROWN.

bold brights®

- glorious green
- green galore
- gable green
- yoyo yellow
- only orange
- real red
- pink passion
- pixie pink
- orchid opulence
- lovely lilac
- brilliant blue
- tempting turquoise

earth elements®

- chocolate chip
- close to cocoa
- creamy caramel
- more mustard
- pumpkin pie
- really rust
- ruby red
- cameo coral
- summer sun
- old olive
- garden green
- not quite navy

rich regals®

- bordering blue
- brocade blue
- ballet blue
- night of navy
- taken with teal
- handsome hunter
- always artichoke
- so saffron
- regal rose
- rose red
- bravo burgundy
- elegant eggplant

soft subtles®

- perfect plum
- pale plum
- pretty in pink
- blush blossom
- apricot appeal
- barely banana
- certainly celery
- mellow moss
- sage shadow
- bashful blue
- almost amethyst
- lavender lace

*Colors, item numbers, and prices for items available in
our color families are listed on pages 154-157.*

join the family

Join thousands of Stampin' Up! demonstrators who share a love of creativity and own their own businesses. You'll receive exceptional support along the way. Your demonstrator can help you, and Stampin' Up! provides a monthly magazine, an informative web site, company events, and much more. Ask your demonstrator how you can join the family!

Get more information about joining Stampin' Up! by contacting your demonstrator and visiting the site below.

www.stampinup.com
1-800-STAMP UP

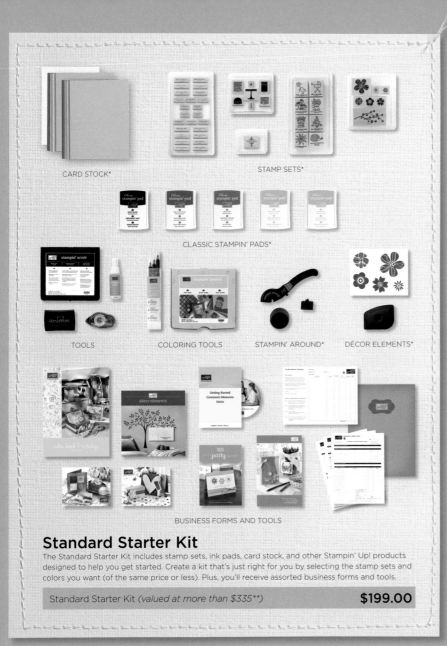

CARD STOCK*

STAMP SETS*

CLASSIC STAMPIN' PADS*

TOOLS   COLORING TOOLS   STAMPIN' AROUND*   DÉCOR ELEMENTS*

BUSINESS FORMS AND TOOLS

Standard Starter Kit

The Standard Starter Kit includes stamp sets, ink pads, card stock, and other Stampin' Up! products designed to help you get started. Create a kit that's just right for you by selecting the stamp sets and colors you want (of the same price or less). Plus, you'll receive assorted business forms and tools.

Standard Starter Kit *(valued at more than $335**)*   **$199.00**

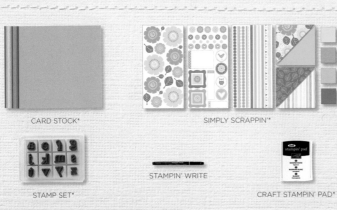

CARD STOCK*   SIMPLY SCRAPPIN'*

STAMP SET*   STAMPIN' WRITE   CRAFT STAMPIN' PAD*

Stampin' Memories Add-on

Designed for the crafter with an interest in scrapbooking, the Stampin' Memories Add-On enhances the Standard Starter Kit by including products tailored for this popular pastime. Choose the color, assortment, and stamp set that reflects your style.

Stampin' Memories Add-On *(valued at more than $80**)*   **$50.00**

love what you do

Every demonstrator creates a business that's just right for her. When you join Stampin' Up!, you'll do the same. Create a full-time business, or work a few days a month to earn extra money. When you can set your own work schedule, you're sure to love what you do as a demonstrator.

share what you love

Enjoy the social rewards of being a Stampin' Up! demonstrator by finding people who share your interests and sharing your love of creativity. With Stampin' Up!, you can make your work fun! You can meet new people and strengthen current friendships.

enjoy creativity

Our Starter Kit includes the Stampin' Up! products and business supplies you need to get started right away. You can customize your kit—choose your own stamp sets and other select products that will inspire you to be creative. Plus you'll gain access to our Demonstrator Web Site, which offers hundreds of project ideas to motivate you.

host a workshop!

You can earn exclusive stamp sets and other Stampin' Up! products (see pages 12-18) by hosting a qualifying workshop. Enjoy a fun event with your friends. Get a free catalog from your demonstrator. When you receive these and other benefits, you'll see why thousands of workshops are held every year.

socialize

Workshops are about more than the products—they're about the people. Spend quality time with your family, friends, and neighbors as you laugh, learn, and create together. You'll enjoy it so much you'll want to schedule another workshop.

discover the new

At your workshop, your demonstrator will show you a variety of products and techniques. Whether you are new to Stampin' Up! or are a longtime crafter, you'll discover new products and get new ideas. Talk to your demonstrator about hosting a workshop tailored to your interests.

creative coaching

Your demonstrator will share her expert knowledge as she demonstrates projects and offers tips and techniques. Plus, your demonstrator may provide a hands-on creative experience, so you can try the products yourself. You'll love the process of creating a project of your own.

discover what you can earn

net workshop total	hostess sets			hostess awards
	level 1	level 2	level 3	free merchandise totaling up to:
$150.00–$199.99	choose 1	—	—	$15.00
$200.00–$249.99	choose 1	—	—	$20.00
$250.00–$299.99	choose 1	—	—	$25.00
$300.00–$349.99	choose 1 or choose 1		—	$35.00
$350.00–$399.99	choose 1 or choose 1		—	$40.00
$400.00–$449.99	choose 2	—	—	$45.00
or				
	choose 1	choose 1	—	
$450.00–$499.99	choose 2	—	—	$50.00
or				
	choose 1	choose 1	—	
$500.00–$549.99	choose 3	—	—	$60.00
or				
	choose 2	choose 1	—	
or				
	choose 1	—	choose 1	
$550.00–$599.99	choose 3	—	—	$65.00
or				
	choose 2	choose 1	—	
or				
	choose 1	—	choose 1	
$600.00–$649.99	choose 2	choose 1	—	$75.00
or				
	choose 1	choose 2	—	
or				
	—	choose 1	choose 1	
or				
	choose 3	—	—	
or				
	choose 1	—	choose 1	
$650.00–$699.99	choose 2	choose 1	—	$85.00
or				
	choose 1	choose 2	—	
or				
	—	choose 1	choose 1	
or				
	choose 3	—	—	
or				
	choose 1	—	choose 1	
$700.00–$749.99	choose 2	—	choose 1	$95.00
or				
	choose 1	choose 1	choose 1	
or				
	—	—	choose 2	
or				
	choose 3	—	—	
or				
	choose 2	choose 1	—	
or				
	choose 1	choose 2	—	
$750.00+	choose 2	—	choose 1	$100 plus 15% of amount over $750.00
or				
	choose 1	choose 1	choose 1	
or				
	—	—	choose 2	
or				
	choose 3	—	—	
or				
	choose 2	choose 1	—	
or				
	choose 1	choose 2	—	

shipping & handling is not charged on hostess benefits

earn your wish list

Earning free products is one of the perks of being a Stampin' Up! hostess. Make a list of items you want, then review the chart to find out how to earn them. You can select exclusive hostess sets available only to hostesses (pages 12-18). You can also earn hostess awards to use toward merchandise of your choice!

Out of the Box
SET OF 6
115342 *(level 1)*

There is a calmness to a life lived in gratitude, a quiet joy.
—Ralph H. Blum

Country Morning
SET OF 4
115334 *(level 1)*

ESP | **Hermoso amanecer** 116726 | FRA | **Matin champêtre** 116550

love bugs

cute as a bug

Love Bug
SET OF 6
115233 *(level 1)*

FRA | **Petit amour** 116558

SHOWN IN REALLY RUST

Patterns Pack Designer Series Paper III

Hostesses can choose this 6" x 6" pad of our Patterns Designer Series paper. This pack features an assortment of 5 colors never before offered in the Patterns line. 60 sheets: 2 ea. of 6 double-sided designs in each color.

	116234	Patterns Pack III	level 1
		Ruby Red, Mellow Moss, Sahara Sand, Really Rust, Night of Navy	

The greatest gift is a portion of thyself.
—Ralph Waldo Emerson

	Holiday Best	SET OF
	(level 1) 115364	4
Celebraciones especiales 116730	ESP	Expressions festives 116554 FRA

	Of the Earth	SET OF
	(level 1) 115336	4
De la naturaleza 116734 ESP		Vérités terrestres 116560 FRA

Enjoy the Christmas Punch set with its coordinating punches found on page 186.

A merry little *Christmas* to you

to:

from:

have a **holly jolly** christmas

'tis the season!

 Temporada Navideña 116724   **Noël en tête** 116548

SET OF **7** | **Christmas Punch**
115366 *(level 2)*

Your *friendship* means the world to me.

SET OF **4** | **Wings of Friendship**
114308 *(level 2)*

Alas de amistad 116466   **Les ailes de l'amitié** 116564

> Wherever you go,
> go with all your heart.
>
> ~Confucius

Arte Oriental **ESP** 116460   Art Asiatique **FRA** 116546

Asian Artistry | SET OF
(level 2) 114399 | 5

SWEET BB

ADMIT IT

HB2U

OWLWAYS

XOXOXO

TRU FRND

Admítelo **ESP** 116458   Billet doux **FRA** 116544

Admit It | SET OF
(level 2) 113772 | 6

Paige
September
2008

five

Today is your special day, your 5th birthday. Five years that
have gone by too fast. Five years that you have blessed my life.

I can't wait to see what the next five years will bring!

May today be the beginning
of a love that lasts forever.

Best Wishes

Thinking of You

Hope your birthday is as
happy as happy gets!

Kind, genuine, caring, fun ... you're many
things, but most of all you're loved.

Thanks So Much

Hope you feel
better soon.

Just want you to know how much
your thoughtfulness is appreciated.

...and it's all good!

SET OF
12   **Kind & Caring Thoughts**
115324 *(level 3)*

 ESP   **Pensamientos bondadosos**
116732

FRA   **Avec toute mon affection**
116556

Use your Paper Snips to cut out stamped images. You can rearrange or omit any part of an image by cutting out the pieces.

a halloween hi!   warm winter wishes   so happy to have a friend like you.   sweetest ever

Cut out shapes from our Designer Series paper to create a fabulous focal point.

Lovely Flowers Bundle

This level 3 hostess bundle includes 2 sheets of Lovely Lines Rub-Ons (1 ea. Chocolate Chip and Whisper White), 9 sheets of 12" x 12" double-sided Designer Series paper (3 ea. in 3 designs), and the Flower Lines stamp set.

| 116916 | Lovely Flowers Bundle | level 3 |

FLOWER LINES STAMP ARTWORK (DOUBLE-MOUNTED SET OF 4)

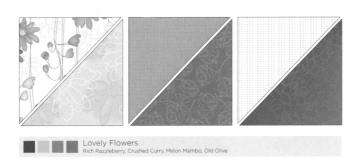

Lovely Flowers
Rich Razzleberry, Crushed Curry, Melon Mambo, Old Olive

Lovely Lines Rub-Ons
Whisper White, Chocolate Chip

RUB-ONS SHOWN AT 35% WITH A SMALL PORTION OF THE IMAGE SHOWN AT ACTUAL SIZE
PAPER PATTERN SWATCHES SHOWN AT 25%

holidays

halloween
COLLECTION

With our products, you won't be haunted by a lack of creativity. Your dilemma will be choosing between all the amazing options. Use the Spooky Treats Rub-Ons to make quick Halloween treats.

try this technique...

1.

2.

3.

1. Position the Rub-On image. **2.** Rub the image with an applicator. **3.** Carefully peel off the transfer sheet.

Spooky Treats Rub-Ons
115729 **$10.95**
page 177

Pumpkin Pie 1/4" Grosgrain Ribbon
109030 **$4.95**
page 183

Cast-a-Spell Designer Series Paper
115677 **$9.95**
page 161

From the Crypt | SET OF 4
115460 **$22.95**

SET OF 4 | **House of Haunts**
111574 **$22.95**

BATTY F

happy halloween · trick-or-treat · happy halloween

SCAREDY-CAT

Haunting*
112480 **$8.50** *(jumbo)*

Batty*
109689 **$8.50** *(jumbo)*

Bad to the bone • Bad to the bone • Bad to the bone

Fangs for the memories • Fangs for the memories • Fangs for the memories

Creepy crawly, oh my golly • Creepy crawly, oh my golly

Trick or treat, smell my feet • Trick or treat, smell my feet

I'm batty for you • I'm batty for you • I'm batty for you

You light up the place with that smile on your face • You light up the place

The ghostess with the mostest • The ghostess with the mostest

Scaredy-cat • Scaredy-cat • Scaredy-cat • Scaredy-cat

Batty for You | SET OF 8
116576 **$23.95**

FREE KISSES

BEST WITCHES!

HALLOWEEN IS A HOOT!

FREE KISSES

Halloween Hoot | SET OF 11
111582 **$29.95**

happy haunting!

SET OF 4 | **Scary Skeleton**
113244 **$13.95**

ESP | Esqueleto tenebroso
116468

YUM • YUM • YUM • YUM • YUM • YUM • YUM

IF YOU WANT A *tasty sweet*, BE SURE TO HOLLER...
tricK·or·treat

SET OF 6 | **Tasty Sweet**
111698 **$19.95**

halloween frights

spooky nights

SET OF 8 | **Halloween Frights**
111766 **$15.95** *(double-mounted)*

ESP | Sustos de Halloween
111782

FRA | Frissons d'Halloween
111862

Frightful Fence
113632 **$8.50** *(jumbo)*

simple style

Give your projects added style by accenting them with brads, buttons, and more. Clear Rhinestone brads add emphasis to the skull on this card. The handheld punch is the perfect tool to apply brads with.

Clear Rhinestone Brads
113144 **$10.95** *page 179*

1/16" Circle Handheld Punch
101227 **$8.95** *page 186*

All Hallow's Eve* | SET OF
113264 **$17.95** | 1

happy fright night to you

hal·low·een (hăl/ə-wēn/) *n*
1. October 31, celebrated by children of all ages. 2. Dressing up, trick-or-treat, bob for apples, cider sweet. 3. Jack-o'-lanterns, squeals of fright, a happy, dandy, candy night!

Eat, Drink & Be Scary | SET OF
111764 **$18.95** | 5

Web |
115666 **$6.50**

Arachnophobia |
108017 **$6.50**

SET OF
6 | **Autumn Harvest**
110372 **$17.95**

SEASON of THANKS
SEASON of BLESSINGS
SEASON of LOVE

SET OF
4 | **Harvest Home**
111642 **$23.95**

| **Fall Harvest**
112478 **$6.50**

rockin' ribbon

Nothing embellishes a project like ribbon, and we offer it in dozens of shades to suit any season. From ribbons to trims—we offer a style for all projects.

Chocolate Chip
1-1/4" Striped Grosgrain Ribbon
115617 **$8.95** *page 183*

Linen Thread
104199 **$4.50** *page 183*

{GRATEFUL}

so thankful for you and all that you do

Happy THANKSGIVING, happy FALL, happy BLESSINGS to one and all.

thankful

Falling Leaves
115368 **$21.95**   SET OF 9

appreciation

THANKFULNESS

grateful

Gratitude

GRATITUDE

can transform common days

into THANKSGIVINGS.

Gratitude is heaven itself.
~William Blake

In every thing give THANKS.

Blessings

brighten when we count them.

Bright Blessings
(jumbo) 115626 **$8.50**

christmas
COLLECTION

Ornaments aren't just for trees any more. String them across a table to add festive décor to any home or workspace. You can also use the ornaments as gift tags.

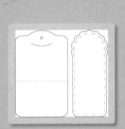

Stampin' Up! Two Tags Bigz Die
115954 **$21.95**
page 198

Merry Moments Designer Series Paper
115672 **$9.95**
page 160

Treat Boxes
115690 **$3.95**
page 159

Real Red 3/4" Polka-Dot Grosgrain Ribbon
115608 **$8.95**
page 183

May the joy and love you feel this holiday season extend to every day throughout the year.

Merry Christmas

| SET OF 4 | **Tree Trimmings** 116722 **$14.95** |

SET OF 2	**Christmas Greetings** 115448 **$10.95**
ESP	Saludos navideños 116738
FRA	Tous mes vœux pour Noël 116704

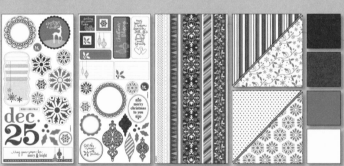

Christmas Jingle Simply Scrappin'®
115696 **$19.95**
page 165

Jumbo Snowflake Punch
116628 **$15.95**
page 186

Holiday Photo Card Kit
115667 **$19.95**
page 175

A GIFT FOR:

WITH ♥ FROM:

Sweet Season
116471 **$18.95**
SET OF 4

season of white, cold the night,
stars shine bright, all is right.

Two Cool Dudes
SET OF 4 | 111708 **$21.95**

Each of the Spotlight on Christmas
stamps coordinates with a punch.
Check out the selection on page 186.

Spotlight on Christmas
SET OF 6 | 111694 **$22.95**

FRA Pleins feux sur Noël
111740

give it your best shot

Use our Big Shot dies to cut through many materials such as window sheets, chipboard, fabric, and more.

Serif Essentials Alphabet Bigz Dies
113464 **$149.95** *page 199*

also used on this page...

Medium Window Sheets
114323 **$4.95** *page 158*

have a holly, jolly Christmas!

to:

from:

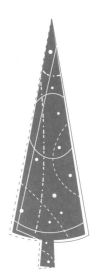

Una alegre y feliz Navidad **ESP** 112889   Un merveilleux Noël **FRA** 113522

A Holly, Jolly Christmas SET OF 8
111558 **$26.95**

Jolly
112479 **$6.50**

ornamental

With our Big Shot dies, you can create wood ornaments as seen here, plus dozens of other festive accents. See our selection of dies on pages 195–202.

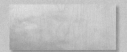

Snowflake #2 Originals Die
113460 **$15.95** *page 202*

Texture Cuts Wood Sheets
116309 **$9.95** *page 158*

also used on this page...

Real Red 1" Double-Stitched Grosgrain Ribbon
115607 **$8.95** *page 182*

hand stamped

| SET OF 8 | **Season of Joy** |
| 110384 **$26.95** |

merry christmas

jingle all the way

jingle all the way

Little Sam was so cute when we sat down to write Santa a list of all the things he wanted for Christmas.

Topping the list was Sam's wish for a baby brother. We shot this photo right after we told Sam the news that his baby brother was due in March.

December 2008

Christmas Classics
111566 $24.95 | SET OF 6

noel

MERRY CHRISTMAS

Jolly surprises, a tree shining bright—
Mistletoe kisses, a home filled with light.
Hearts that are merry, a time of good cheer—
Wishing all this and a Happy New Year!

Season's Greetings

Wishing you a never-ending season of love and peace.

Happy Holidays

Joy expressed,
Love shared,
a Miracle celebrated.

Warmest greetings of the season and every good wish for the coming year.

Many Merry Messages
116586 $34.95 | SET OF 8

At Christmas,
play and make
good cheer,
for Christmas
comes but once
a year.

~Thomas Tusser

SET OF
3 | **Good Cheer**
115326 **$22.95**

Though far and wide
on earth we roam,
at Christmastime
our hearts come home.

A Christmas Wish...

SET OF
3 | **Home for Christmas**
111756 **$18.95**

FRA | Vœu des Fêtes
111866

To:

From:

Post Card

THIS SIDE IS FOR THE ADDRESS ONLY

SANTA POST
NORTH POLE
DEC 25

Do not open 'til
Dec. 25

Courrier d'hiver FRA
111868

♡ | **Winter Post** | SET OF
111780 **$26.95** | 7

*M*ay the peace and joy
of the season be with you
throughout the new year

Season's Greetings

Scenic Season | SET OF
115354 **$24.95** | 2

Soft Holly
112968 **$6.50**

HOLIDAYS   35

Wishing you a
never-ending season
of love and peace.

Use Stampin' Dimensionals® to make your focal point stand out, as featured on the Season's Greetings card. The snowflake image comes to life.

Season's Greetings

May the true spirit
of Christmas
fill your heart with peace,
your home with love.

SET OF 6	**Snow Swirled**
	111690 **$24.95**

FRA **Folies de flocons**
111734

SET OF 4	**Holy Triptych**
	110370 **$32.95**

Christ is Born

Let the heavens rejoice and the earth be glad.
~ Psalm 96:11

Wishing you the joy and wonder
of the first Christmas.

Le Christ est né FRA
112863

Christ Is Born | SET OF
111612 **$20.95** | 3

May the blessings of
PEACE, HOPE & LOVE
be your gifts this Christmas and
throughout the coming year.

Christmas Wishes

Gifts of Christmas | SET OF
115372 **$18.95** | 3

A wish for peace and happiness
at Christmas
and throughout the new year.

SET OF
3 | **A Wish for Peace**
111614 **$16.95**

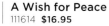

*M*erry *C*hristmas

*M*ay all the blessings
of the season
fill your heart and home
with joy.

SET OF
4 | **A Cardinal Christmas**
111760 **$23.95**

For unto you is born this day in the city of David a Saviour, which is Christ the Lord.

Luke 2:11

May your season be touched with the simple grace of Christ's love.

Merry Christmas!

Cœur en paix 111870 **FRA** Nacimiento 112935 **ESP**

Season of Simple Grace
111778 **$25.95** | SET OF 6

HAPPY KWANZAA!

UMOJA · KUJICHAGULIA · UJIMA · UJAMAA · NIA · KUUMBA · IMANI

Happy Kwanzaa
111640 **$15.95** | SET OF 4

• Use the Crop-A-Dile to dry emboss your cards and other stamping projects like the row of circles on the Happy Hanukkah card. It's fun and easy and adds the perfect finishing touch.

KWANZAA

Happy Hanukkah

HAPPY HANUKKAH

HAPPY bar mitzvah   **HAPPY** bat mitzvah

Shalom Sayings
111686 **$15.95** | SET OF 4

Enhance a line-art image by watercoloring it with our Aqua Painter®. Use a balance of light and dark colors to create a pleasing image.

to:
FROM:

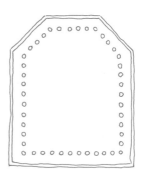

HAPPY HOLidays
a GiFT FOR YOU
MERRY CHRISTMAS
Let it SNOW
FROM OUR HOUSE to YOURS

great gifts

The holidays are a time of giving. With our cellophane bags and your favorite seasonal stamp set, you can make small gifts quickly for everyone on your list.

Cellophane Bags
page 159

Stampin' Up! Top Note Bigz Die
113463 **$21.95** *page 198*

MAY YOUR SEASON BE
Sparkly & bright!

Sparkly & Bright | SET OF **6**
115346 **$17.95**

Sparkling*
(jumbo) 116444 **$8.50**

Santa's Lineup*
(jumbo) 113120 **$8.50**

Embellish a gift bag with a coordinating color of ribbon around the top edge.

Happy Holidays

christmas fishes to all!

shellebrate the season

SET OF 5 | **Shellebrate**
111688 **$18.95**

It's the jolliest, lightest, merriest, brightest, most wonderful time of the year!

SET OF 4 | **Jolliest Time of the Year**
116584 **$20.95**

You lassoed my heart, darlin'!

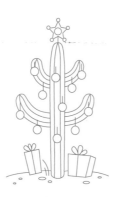

Yee haw and Merry Christmas!

Have a rootin' tootin' Happy Halloween!

Happy Easter, buckaroo!

SET OF 4 | **Yippee Kiyay Holiday**
114369 **$19.95**

Use brads to embellish your handcrafted creations. Our selection of colors and styles means you're sure to find the right one for your project.

Holiday Lineup
111648 $21.95

SET OF 3

Easter Wishes

Merry CHRISTMAS

HAPPY HALLOWEEN

Peace Love Joy

hugs & kisses

for you

Mr. & Mrs.

HAPPY FATHER'S DAY

happy birthday

❈{ thank you }❈

HAPPY *mother's* DAY

MY *dear* KIND & *wonderful* FRIEND

All Holidays
114916 $34.95

SET OF 12

Fêtes diverses
116253

FRA

HOLIDAYS   **43**

friend to friend

Use the Heart to Heart punch (page 186) to cut out the small heart images in the Love You Much set. You'll have instant embellishments for your projects!

thank you

friend to friend

you much

| SET OF 6 | **Love You Much** 113756 **$25.95** | | ESP | **Te quiero mucho** 114022 | FRA | **J't'aime beaucoup** 115295 |

xoxoxo *my* **mom** thank *you* dear **dad**

| SET OF 28 | **Holiday Blitz** 114982 **$38.95** | | FRA | **Tourbillon des Fêtes** 116257 |

wishing
you a
happy
heart

happy valentine's day

Olivia, February 14, 2009

{FEB. 14}

i♥u

happy valentine's day

Un cœur joyeux
111864 **FRA**

A Happy Heart | SET OF 6
111758 **$22.95**

i still ♥ you!

love love love

you and moi?
ooh la la!

♥u

You & Moi | SET OF 6
111716 **$12.95**

fishes, wishes & kisses

Chew, chew, I like you!

Whoo's your valentine?

Whoo's Your Valentine? | SET OF 4
115344 **$19.95**

i still ♥ you!

Hearts O' Plenty
115621 **$6.50**

The "Happy Easter" and "You crack me up" greetings from the A Good Egg set share one wood block. Simply ink and stamp the image you need. Use one greeting on the inside and one on the outside of your card.

HAPPY FATHER'S DAY!

C

happy future

you're the icing on the cake!

for your shower

i just realized that I'm turning into my mother...

{lucky me!}

THOUGHTFUL KIND
INSPIRING GENTLE
dad
BRAVE LOVING TRUE
STRONG CARING

happy easter

thanks so much

 ESP Ocho saludos geniales
115421   **FRA** Huit souhaits sympas
114643

you crack me up

happy easter

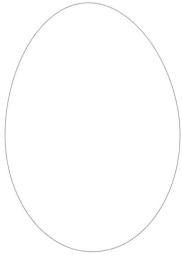

occasions

wedding
COLLECTION

Our wedding collection offers graceful, elegant stamp sets and accessories designed to commemorate that special day. From invitations and place settings to thank-you cards and scrapbook pages, this collection has it all.

Stampin' Up! Perfect Setting Bigz XL Die
115961 **$42.95**
page 200

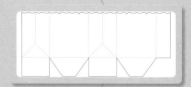

Stampin' Up! Fancy Favor Bigz XL Die
115965 **$39.95**
page 200

Stampin' Up! Elegant Bouquet Textured Impressions Folder
115964 **$7.95**
page 195

Bride Specialty Paper
115669 **$13.95**
page 158

Wedding Words Rub-Ons
115727 **$10.95**
page 177

Stampin' Up! Finial Press Textured Impressions Folder
115963 **$7.95**
page 195

SET OF 7 | **Wedding Sweet**
115466 **$25.95**

Sweet Swirls
115523 **$6.50**

Forever Flowers
111252 **$6.50**

mr. mrs.

TOGETHER
Forever

We're engaged!

Pour toujours
113550 | FRA

Together Forever
115100 $22.95 | SET OF 6

Monogram Sweet | SET OF 28
115462 **$31.95**

Wedding Personalized Stamp

One line of personalized text (date), up to 16 characters. Spaces count as a character; capitals count as 2 spaces.

| 116480 Special Date* | $10.95 |

12.08.2010

Wedding Personalized Stamp

Choose up to 3 lines of text (for name, in all caps), up to 26 characters per line. Spaces count as a character.

| 115464 Yours and Mine* | $15.95 |

EMMA MARIE HARRISON

AND

MICHAEL ALEX ROBINSON

a touch of texture

Create a textured background with a ruler and a bone folder (page 188). Just follow the steps below.

1.

2.

1. At evenly spaced intervals, score the card stock with a bone folder.
2. Change direction and score again to create a diamond shape.

May God bless you...

on your Special day

on your Wedding day

as you start your Married Life

on your First Communion

on your Baptism day

SET OF 8 | **Special Blessings**
113411 **$19.95** *(double-mounted)*

ESP Benediciones especiales
114026

May your
HAPPILY EVER AFTER
begin with
a beautiful today.

SET OF 4 | **Ever After**
113401 **$22.95**

 Romance
115121 **$6.50**

a friend is someone
who makes it easy

simply said
from the heart...
thank you

Amitié FRA
116247

Simply Said | SET OF 11
115066 **$28.95**

Scatter Sunshine | (jumbo) 107213 **$8.50**

Kindness | (jumbo) 106750 **$8.50**

Thinking of You...

Please know that I care.

Sharing in your Sorrow

terrific twill

Create customized twill tape by selecting your favorite image. First, color the stamp with our Watercolor Wonder™ Crayons. Mist Twill Tape with water and then stamp the colored image. The bough in Thoughts & Prayers creates an elegant floral pattern.

Twill Tape
105245 **$5.95** *page 183*

Rich Regals
Watercolor Wonder Crayons
106698 **$19.95** *page 154*

Praying for friends to comfort you, faith to uphold you, and loving memories to heal your heart.

Wishing you a quick and complete recovery.

GET WELL SOON

Praying for You...

Sending thoughts of love and praying for the Lord to sustain you with bright and restful days.

SET OF 8 | **Thoughts & Prayers**
113252 **$25.95** *(double-mounted)*

Earth has no sorrow that heaven cannot heal.

– Thomas Moore

WITH HEARTFELT Sympathy

Your loved one will always be as close as a memory, and the God of all comfort as close as a prayer.

SET OF 4 | **Close As a Memory**
114946 **$20.95**

FRA **Près du cœur**
116273

Earth has no sorrow that heaven cannot heal.
~Thomas Moore

A kind word is like a spring day.

Each day of life is a precious gift from God.
~Charles H. Spurgeon

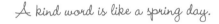
A kind word is like a spring day.

♡ | **A Kind Word** | SET OF
| 113194 **$21.95** | 4

God is,
and all
is well.
~John Whittier

Each day of life is a
precious gift from God.
~Charles H. Spurgeon

God is our refuge
and strength,
therefore we will
not fear.
Psalm 46:1, 2

God is not too
great
to be concerned
about our
smallest wishes.

In those times
I can't seem to
find God, I rest
in the assurance
He knows how to
find me.
~Neva Coyle

Refuge and Strength | SET OF
115056 **$23.95** | 7

back to school

Give your projects the look of the schoolroom with our Spiral punch. Your card stock will look like it came from a notebook. You can also use this punch to add pages to our art journals.

Spiral Punch
108341 **$10.95**
page 186

things i love...

shopping

new shoes

chocolate

but most of all
...YOU!

SET OF 6	**Things I Love** 115229 **$15.95**

always on my mind—
forever in my heart.

{EVERYTHING}

you mean everything to me.

SET OF 11	**Always** 113620 **$28.95**	FRA	**Toujours** 116285

	Always in Bloom 113834 **$6.50**

*I count myself
in nothing else
so happy
as in a soul
remembering
my good friends.*

*Lavender
{devotion}*

*Basil
{blessings}*

*May happiness
touch your life today
as warmly as you
have touched the lives
of others.*

*Rosemary
{remembrance}*

I didn't forget your birthday.
I'm just fashionably late!

Lavender
{devotion}

*Thanks for blessing
my life with you.*

*I'm here
for you ...
just as
you've
always
been there
for me.*

*Thyme
{happiness}*

Herb Expressions | SET OF
113224 **$32.95** | 8

Cinderella is proof
that a new pair of *shoes*
can *change* your life!

*Whether you're a good witch
or a bad witch,
it's all about the shoes!*

Change of a dress.

*Give a girl the correct footwear
and she can conquer the world!*

~ Bette Midler

I didn't forget your birthday.
I'm just fashionably late!

Humor in High Heels | SET OF
111652 **$26.95** | 10

Scoring adds a subtle texture to the All Spruced Up card. See page 50 to learn how to create it.

ALL SPRUCED UP

TOGETHER FOREVER

GET WELL WISHES

HAPPY NEW BABY

THANKS FOR SHARING YOU WITH ME

CONGRATULATIONS

THANKS... I NEEDED THAT

HAPPY BIRTHDAY WISHES

SET OF 8 | **Fun & Fast Notes**
113500 **$33.95**

ESP | Notas rápidas y divertidas
112915

FRA | Petits mots rigolos
113546

Fast Flowers
109679 **$6.50**

cut it out

Stamp an image on our Designer Series paper to give it instant color and appeal. Then cut out the image, as featured on our Bon Appétit project.

So Saffron Patterns Designer Series Paper
112152 **$9.95** *page 161*

Paper Snips
103579 **$9.95** *page 191*

Earth Elements Brads
106955 **$8.95** *page 179*

Grandma's Oatmeal Raisin Cookies

1/2 cup butter, softened
1/2 cup butter flavored shortening
1 cup packed light brown sugar
1/2 cup white sugar
2 eggs
1 teaspoon vanilla extract

1 1/2 cups all-purpose flour
1 teaspoon baking soda
1 teaspoon ground cinnamon
1/2 teaspoon ground cloves
1/2 teaspoon salt
3 cups rolled oats
1 cup raisins

DIRECTIONS:

1. Preheat oven to 350 degrees F (175 degrees C).

2. In a large bowl, cream together butter, butter flavored shortening, brown sugar, white sugar, eggs, and vanilla. Combine flour, baking soda, cinnamon, cloves, and salt; stir into the creamed mixture. Stir in the oats and raisins. Drop by teaspoonfuls onto ungreased cookie sheets.

3. Bake for 10 to 12 minutes in the preheated oven. Allow cookies to cool for 2 minutes on the cookie sheet before transferring to a wire rack to cool completely. Store in an airtight container.

Voilà
115102 **$25.95**   SET OF 6

Voilà to Go
115104 **$17.95**   SET OF 6

merry christmas!

friends for the long haul

Loads of Love!

wishing you loads of holiday cheer!

merry christmas!

thought you could use a little pickup!

driving by with a birthday "Hi"!

just moved!

eggstra special easter wishes!

happy harvest

friends for the long haul

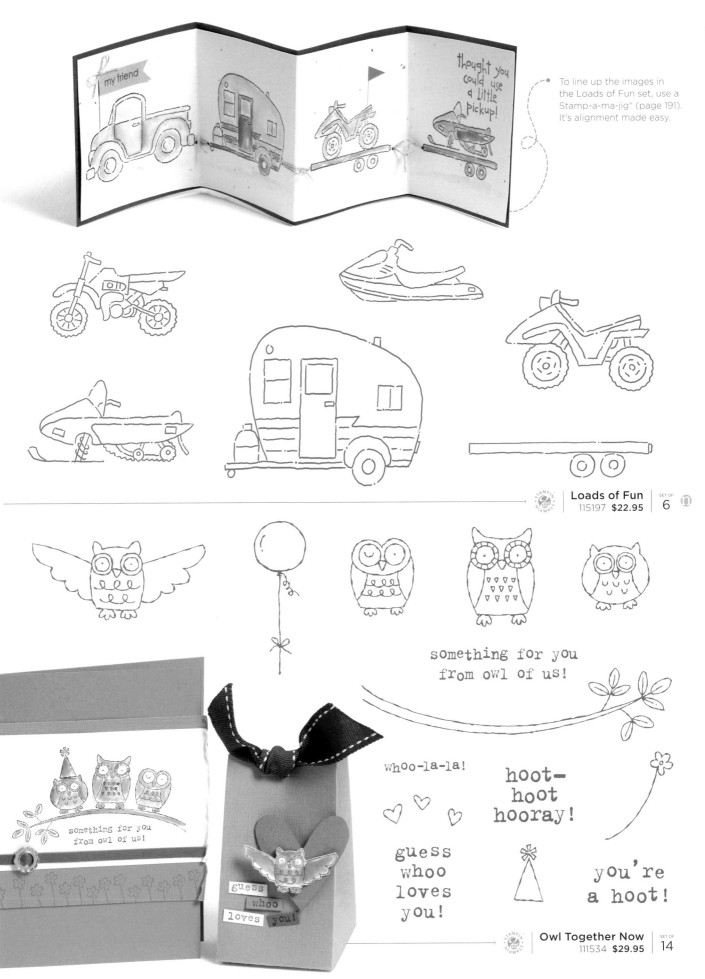

my friend

thought you could use a little pickup!

To line up the images in the Loads of Fun set, use a Stamp-a-ma-jig® (page 191). It's alignment made easy.

Loads of Fun
115197 **$22.95**
SET OF 6

something for you from owl of us!

whoo-la-la!

hoot-hoot hooray!

guess whoo loves you!

you're a hoot!

Owl Together Now
111534 **$29.95**
SET OF 14

OCCASIONS

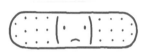

get well soon

Heard you're sick as a dog

Wellness Wishes
SET OF 3 | 115356 **$14.95**

Hip-hippo-ray!

Love you a latte!

Thank ewe!

You're a blast!

Purrrfect!

Get whale soon!

Happy bird-day!

I stink you're sweet!

Pun Fun
SET OF 8 | 115054 **$32.95**

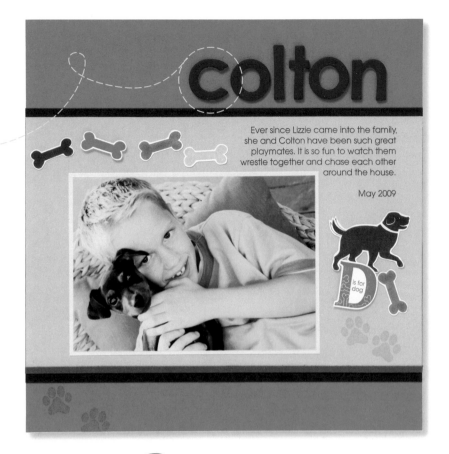

colton

Ever since Lizzie came into the family, she and Colton have been such great playmates. It is so fun to watch them wrestle together and chase each other around the house.

May 2009

D is for dog

so sorry for the loss of your best friend.

a dog wags its tail with its heart.
~Martin Buxbaum

D is for dog

D Is for Dog | SET OF 6
115784 **$15.95**

so sorry for the loss of your little friend.

C is for cat

as every cat owner knows, nobody owns a cat.
~Ellen Perry Berkeley

as every cat owner knows, nobody owns a cat.
~Ellen Perry Berkeley

C Is for Cat | SET OF 6
115764 **$15.95**

P Is for Paw
115620 **$6.50**

SET OF 5 | **Animal Crackers**
113395 **$19.95**

SET OF 6 | **Cheers to You**
114944 **$17.95**

FRA | Tchin-Tchin
116279

 | **Cheers**
113122 **$6.50**

Stamp with StāzOn ink for an image that won't smear. This permanent ink is a must-have for your watercoloring creations!

thanks so very much

hello

peek-a-boo...someone new!

i love you this much!

thanks so very much

Build-a-Roo
115948 **$25.95** SET OF 10

It seems only fitting...
...to wish you a happy day!

hello

merci

merci

Chic Boutique
113744 **$26.95** SET OF 7

snowflake glitter

Create glitter-decorated accents with our 2-Way Glue Pen (page 192) and the glitter (page 180) of your choice.

1.

2.

3.

1. Apply glue to image. **2.** Tap glitter on glue. **3.** Lift piece to remove excess glitter.

Wishing you all this... and more!

laughter joy happiness bliss delight

couldn't do without you.

ready, set, snow!

| SET OF 9 | **Best Wishes & More** 111602 **$26.95** | FRA | Meilleurs vœux et plus encore 112855 |

Cornelli Lace
115624 **$8.50** *(jumbo)*

Dotted Lines
111256 **$8.50** *(jumbo)*

thank you

enjoy every moment life the little things

Enjoy Every Moment | SET OF 11
113622 **$31.95**

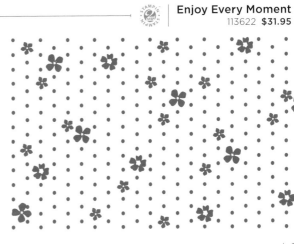

Daisy Dash
(jumbo) 111255 **$8.50**

Delicate Dots
(jumbo) 115622 **$8.50**

thanks for helping me
out of a tight spot.

It's a housewarming party!

sad to see you go

We've moved our doorstep.
Our new address is...

SET OF 5 | **Welcome Home**
113433 **$20.95**

you hit the nail on the head!

he who has the most tools wins.

you came, you sawed, you fixed.
thanks for all you do.

love beyond measure

**thanks for helping me
out of a tight spot.**

SET OF 5 | **Totally Tool**
113256 **$25.95**

With our Pillow Box Bigz die (page 199), you can create boxes such as this one with ease.

Courage is rightly esteemed the first of human qualities, because it is the quality that guarantees all others.

~Winston Churchill

 Courage | SET OF 2
115330 **$19.95**

As you bravely watch over us, may God watch over you.

A real HERO is someone who puts BELIEFS into ACTIONS.

CONGRATULATIONS on your promotion.

THANKS for your dedicated SERVICE and SACRIFICE.

MILES may separate us but LOVE keeps us CLOSE at HEART.

As your LOVED one SERVES our country, may GOD'S BLESSINGS rest upon you.

Service & Sacrifice | SET OF 8
115992 **$18.95**

Hero
(jumbo) 116229 **$8.50**

hope your day
is the sweetest ever!

happy birthday to you

| SET OF 6 | **Crazy for Cupcakes** 111618 **$23.95** | Gâteaux en folie 111750 |

happy birthday

| SET OF 4 | **Bitty Birthday** 114934 **$12.95** |

 | **Cupcakes** 113121 **$6.50**

you take the cake!

party hearty!

...and many more!

Célèbre en grand
111722 (FRA)

Party Hearty | SET OF 9
111532 **$26.95**

*time*to*celebrate!

Celebration
112477 **$6.50**

Use the Simple Birthday Thanks stamp to create thank-you notes. For additional versatility, color the stamp with a marker to eliminate any part of the image, such as the sprinkles on the frosting or the text on the cupcake.

Dear _____,

Thank you for the

_____.

I like it a lot!

Sincerely,

_____

SET OF
1 | **Simple Birthday Thanks**
111546 **$17.95**

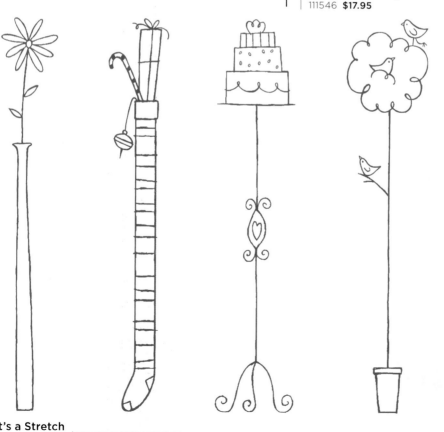

Merry and Bright

SET OF
4 | **It's a Stretch**
111586 **$23.95**

HAPPY EVERYTHING TO YOU!

AMAZING
THOUGHTFUL
SWEET
WONDERFUL
genuine

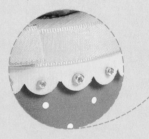

Sobre un pedestal | ESP | Sur un piédestal | FRA
116464 | | 116568

On a Pedestal | SET OF
113814 **$19.95** | 7

ICE CREAM
& presents
AND **CAKE**
OH MY!

birthday bliss

make a wish

May your *layers* be many & your *frosting* be thick

Birthday Bliss | SET OF
115442 **$15.95** | 4

just hoppin'
all is well!

happy together

so hoppy for you!

just hoppin'
all is well!

time's fun when
you're having flies.

SET OF
9 | **Hoppy for You**
113270 **$23.95**

happy together

 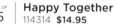

SET OF
5 | **Happy Together**
114314 **$14.95**

Happy Birthday!

Look who's turning...

0 1 2 3 4 5 6 7 8 9

SET OF
8 | **Look Who's Turning**
114403 **$23.95**

growing up

kids birthday
COLLECTIONS

These adorable themed party kits include treat boxes, invitations, and more. They are so much fun, you'll want to throw a party every month!

Pirate Party Kit
116213 **$15.95**
page 175

ⓝ Pirate Personalized Name Stamp
One line of personalized text (for name), up to 26 characters. Spaces count as a character; capitals count as 2 spaces. The word "Captain" counts towards the 26 characters and must be entered on the personalized name stamp form if you wish for it to be included in front of your child's name.

| 115524 | Captain* | $9.95 |

Captain Levi Hansen

ⓝ **SET OF 5** | **Pirate Time**
116718 **$16.95**

Princess Party Kit
116214 **$15.95**
page 174

HAPPY BIRTHDAY
Princess

Princess Time | SET OF
116720 **$16.95** | 6

Jake Johnson · Our little boy forever and always · September 2008

so happy for you!   little cutie

rock-a-bye baby   it's a boy!

it's a girl!

welcome, little one

SET OF 12	**Nursery Necessities** 113506 **$31.95**

FRA **Pouponnages** 113548

Nursery Letters 111258 **$8.50** (jumbo)

BUNDLE OF JOY   THANK YOU

Teddy & Train | SET OF
115219 **$17.95** | 5

date ....

time ....

place ....

I'm kind of a
BIG
D·E·A·L

welcome
little one

Sweet
little
Baby

cute and cuddly

♡ | **Cute & Cuddly** | SET OF
113682 **$26.95** | 6

Our On Board chipboard assortments (pages 184-185) offer a terrific value—dozens of pieces you can use to personalize your projects. Use them plain, cover them with Designer Series paper, or color them with ink.

On Board
Loads of Letters
112084 **$12.95** *page 184*

Noah had such a great time playing football this season. His team was 9-3 and they had so much fun playing together. We could see such an improvement in his team as the season went by and we are so proud of all they accomplished together. His coaches were so patient and all of their hard work really paid off. We can't wait to see what the '09 season has in store for the team!

GAME ON! #1 SCORE Champ ALL★STAR

★ MVP GO TEAM!

SET OF **8** | **Sporting**
115072 **$18.95**

1ST DOWN

SET OF **3** | **Just Baseball**
115002 **$13.95**

SET OF **3** | **Just Football**
115006 **$13.95**

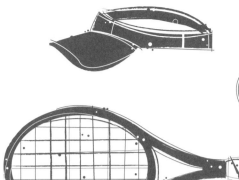

Taylor Hansen's Trading Card

GOAL

Team: Sandy Sorcerers
Position: Center Forward
Age: 11   Height: 4'10"
Coach: Chad Stone

MVP

Just Tennis
115014 **$13.95** | SET OF 3

SURF'S UP

Just Surfing
115012 **$13.95** | SET OF 3

GOAL

Just Soccer
115010 **$13.95** | SET OF 3

SWISH

Just Basketball
115004 **$13.95** | SET OF 3

BMX

Just Riding
115008 **$13.95** | SET OF 3

Stamp one of these silhouette images with VersaMark ink, cover with White Stampin' Emboss powder, and heat emboss for an extreme look that's sure to impress even the most adventurous person in your life!

SET OF
1 | **Extreme Dirt Bike**
115175 **$8.95**

SET OF
1 | **Extreme Guitar**
115328 **$8.95**

SET OF
1 | **Extreme Snowboard**
115177 **$8.95**

SET OF
1 | **Extreme Surfboard**
115173 **$8.95**

SET OF
1 | **Extreme Skateboard**
115179 **$8.95**

Beware Pirates SET OF 5
115187 **$26.95**

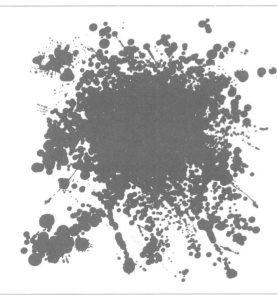

Extreme Elements SET OF 6
115181 **$26.95**

encounters of the creative kind

The fun, adorable images in the Lots of Bots and Greetings, Earthling sets give projects a look that is out of this world!

Star Designer Brads
112572 **$5.95** *page 179*

So Cool Rub-Ons
115725 **$11.95** *page 176*

 SET OF 5 | **Lots of Bots**
115293 **$19.95**

 SET OF 7 | **Greetings, Earthling**
113810 **$21.95**

ERROR
I'm sorry.

HAPPY BIRTHDAY, HUMAN

get well soon

0100100110100100010101000
1001010010101001101010011

GREETINGS, EARTHLING!

Put stars in your skeleton's eyes using our Star punch (page 186). You'll love the versatility.

Choo Choo
113982 **$16.95** | SET OF 5

YOU ROCK!

FRA | **Je t'ai en tête**
112881

Just Jawing | SET OF 6
111660 **$25.95**

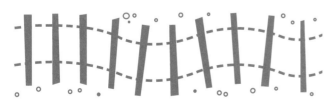 

Right on Track
113838 **$6.50**

Scary Skulls
113119 **$6.50**

family fun

Make personalized projects with our All in the Family set. This set is one children will enjoy, too, so you can make it a family activity!

Circle Scissor Plus
112530 **$29.95** *page 191*

Glass Mat
112531 **$19.95** *page 191*

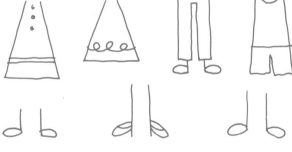

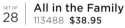

| SET OF 28 | **All in the Family** |
| 113488 **$38.95** |

 Neighborhood
109685 **$8.50** *(jumbo)*

84   GROWING UP   © 1990–2009 STAMPIN' UP!

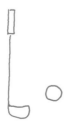

better get
better

from all of
us

• Use our clips (page 179)
to secure ribbon or add
a decorative touch to
your project.

from
all of
us

love
you
much

i like
you

happy birthday

thank you

happy together

happy new baby

let's celebrate

you're invited

Vie de famille · FRA
116297

Family Phrases | SET OF **9**
114960 $19.95

Family Accessories | SET OF **12**
113494 $19.95

Family Accessories Too | SET OF **10**
113760 $19.95

who's got the button?

Our Designer buttons make any project fun. Select from several colors, styles, and sizes.

Playground Designer Buttons
116313 **$7.95** *page 181*

also used on these pages...

Flower Fusion Accents & Elements
110720 **$14.95** *page 180*

magical birthday wishes

 Pony Party
SET OF 11 | 115217 **$20.95**

woot woot!

you're crazy cool!

my bad

you totally rock

 Crazy Cool
SET OF 8 | 115211 **$21.95**

Friends Rock | SET OF 6
113816 $18.95

celebrate

best friends forever

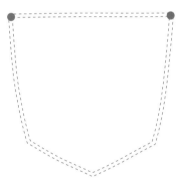

Made 2 Last | SET OF 7
115205 $25.95

Dream
115625 $6.50

Rockin'
115627 $6.50

GROWING UP

re·mem·ber:
To keep in mind a
consideration or r
Memories of days p

Our Define Your Life stamp set (page 150) creates adorable accents for scrapbook pages and other projects, as shown on the Remember page.

also used on this page...

1″ Circle Punch
109046 **$10.95** *page 186*

Tall Tales
Designer Series Paper
115678 **$9.95** *page 161*

re·mem·ber: {ri-měm′bər} *v.*
To keep in mind as worthy of
consideration or recognition.
Memories of days gone by.

Animal Stories
116716 **$15.95**

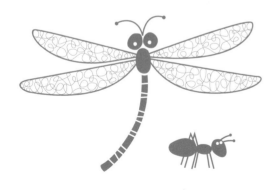

bUgs and
kisses!

cUte
aS a
bUg!

sending
worm
wishes
on your
bUg day!

bUgs and
kisses!

Bugs & Kisses
116580 **$26.95**

Use our tag punches to create tags for gifts, treats, cards, and more! For variety, punch out only a portion of the image as shown on the Bear tag.

dog-gone great!

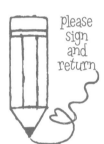

please bee neater

please sign and return

don't forget

please complete

purrrfect!

Teacher's Pet
111554 **$18.95** | SET OF 6

grrreat!

Under the Stars | SET OF 10
111556 **$29.95**

Skeeters
113118 **$6.50**

Frame a greeting or image with our Hodgepodge Hardware (page 178), as shown on the Thanks a Bunch card.

thanks a bunch!

just for you

thanks a bunch!

just for you

SET OF 10 | **Sock Monkey** 111550 **$26.95**

FRA | **Singe-chaussette** 111736

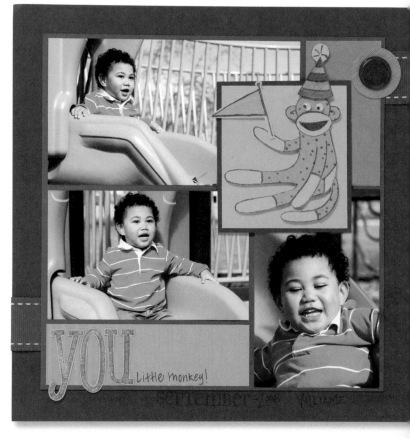

YOU Little monkey!

september 2008 | Volume

SET OF 8 | **Sock Monkey Accessories** 111552 **$21.95**

all natural

Every noble life leaves its fiber interwoven
forever in the work of the world.

Feast

SET OF
6 | **Autumn Days**
115452 **$23.95**

autumn
COLLECTION

Autumn offers a cornucopia of creativity! Make the wreath shown here by securing cutout leaves to a round, metal frame. Overlap the leaves to create a wreath as full as you like.

also try this technique...

1.

2.

3.

1. Place The Tearing Edge on the card stock. **2.** Pull the card stock toward you to create the torn edge. **3.** Distress the edge by hand to create the look shown on the Noble Life card at left.

Autumn Harvest Rub-Ons
115731 **$10.95**
page 177

Leaves #2 Originals Die
113459 **$15.95**
page 202

Orchard Ribbon Originals
116232 **$9.95**
page 182

Autumn Traditions Designer Series Paper
115668 **$9.95**
page 160

Every noble life leaves its fiber interwoven forever in the work of the world.

Farm Life | SET OF **4**
114411 **$21.95**

ALL NATURAL

The Razzle Dazzle set coordinates with our Razzleberry Lemonade Designer Series paper (page 162).

 IT'S GOOD TO DREAM

SET OF 5 | **Razzle Dazzle**
116714 **$18.95**

SET OF 10 | **Greenhouse Garden**
113824 **$25.95**

BIRTHDAY
—CELEBRATIONS—

you're
on my mind

THANK YOU
......FOR YOUR FRIENDSHIP

Pensées en fleurs
111746 FRA

Upsy Daisy | SET OF
111710 **$18.95** | 4

To pay homage to BEAUTY is to admire NATURE; to admire nature is to WORSHIP GOD.
—Unknown

Silhouettes de la nature
112885 FRA

 | **Nature Silhouettes** | SET OF
111542 **$22.95** | 4

live with **passion**

good works
are links that form a chain of love
- Mother Teresa -

SET OF 4   **Inspired by Nature**
111656 **$23.95** (double-mounted)

ESP   **Inspirado por la naturaleza**
112925

FRA   **Inspiré de la nature**
111754

put it in reverse

Enjoy our Soft Suede 1/2" polka-dot grosgrain ribbon. It's reversable—just select the side that best complements your creations.

Soft Suede
1/2" Polka-Dot Grosgrain Ribbon
115612 **$9.95** *page 182*

friend to friend

thanks so much

Silhouettes florales FRA
111726

Pocket Silhouettes | SET OF 6
111672 **$18.95**

Paradise | SET OF 5
113778 **$20.95**

beautiful bling

Our Designer brads make it easy to add bling to your handcrafted creations. With several styles available, there is something for every project.

Filigree Designer Brads
112577 **$5.95** *page 179*

You only live once, but if you do it right, once is enough.

SET OF 5	**Fifth Avenue Floral**
	113734 **$24.95**

blos•som (blŏs′əm) *n.*
1. A flower or cluster of flowers. **2.** The condition of flowering. **3a.** A time of vigor, freshness, and beauty. **b.** A period of maximum development and reaching possibilities.

bloom

SET OF 5	**Bloomin' Beautiful**
	111490 **$25.95**

FRA | **Merveilles en fleur**
111518

A paper-pierced circle adds emphasis to any stamped image. Note how it makes the Thank You card even more lovely.

Thank you for touching my life.

A Rose Is a Rose
111560 **$37.95** | SET OF 14

The way to **KNOW LIFE** *is to* **LOVE** *many things.*
—VAN GOGH

Rêves au menu 112869 FRA

Dreams du Jour
111624 **$18.95** | SET OF 4

ALL NATURAL **99**

Use buttons, Hodgepodge Hardware, and Pretties Kit accents (pages 178-181) to embellish your projects. With so many options to choose from, you're sure to find exactly what you need every time!

Here for You

The HAPPIEST business in the world is that of making **FRIENDS**
~Anne S. Eaton

24-7

SET OF 6 | **Friends 24-7** ♥
113218 **$25.95**

No good thing is PLEASANT without FRI[E]

KINDRED SPIRITS
-Emily Dickinson

My **FRIENDS** Are My ESTATE.

Frie[n] are hard t[o] difficult to and imp[ossible] to forget. E[mily]

you & me
friends
PALS forever and ever

 Friendly Words* ♥
114696 **$8.50** (jumbo)

 Texture
116685 **$8.50** (jumbo)

*COMPLETE WHEEL ART SHOWN ON PAGE 204.

all tied up

Creating bows isn't the only way to use ribbon. Try tying off sections as shown on the Thinking of You card.

**Certainly Celery
5/8" Grosgrain Ribbon**
109050 **$7.95** *page 183*

Linen Thread
104199 **$4.50** *page 183*

Pensées fleuries | **FRA**
113538

Bella's Bloom | SET OF
111600 **$12.95** | 4

Bella's Border |
112476 **$6.50**

Flower Fancy | SET OF
111578 **$36.95** | 10

Frame an image by using our Wide Oval punch (page 186). It's an ideal choice for this Friendship card.

just buzzin' by to say...

have a honey of a day!

SET OF
8 | **Just Buzzin' By**
113228 **$27.95**

*Your friendship is like
a song of spring.*

SET OF
3 | **Spring Song**
115074 **$15.95**

on the edge

Create a scalloped edge with ease using our easy-to-align, exclusive Scallop Edge punch that ensures even placement no matter how long the border.

Scallop Edge Punch
112091 **$15.95** *page 186*

also used on this page...

1/2" Library Clips
112581 **$6.95** *page 179*

A Flower for All Seasons | SET OF **4**
111592 **$14.95**

Peace within makes beauty without.
—English Proverb

Every day holds the possibility of a miracle.
—Elizabeth David

Peace Within | SET OF **4**
114312 **$22.95**

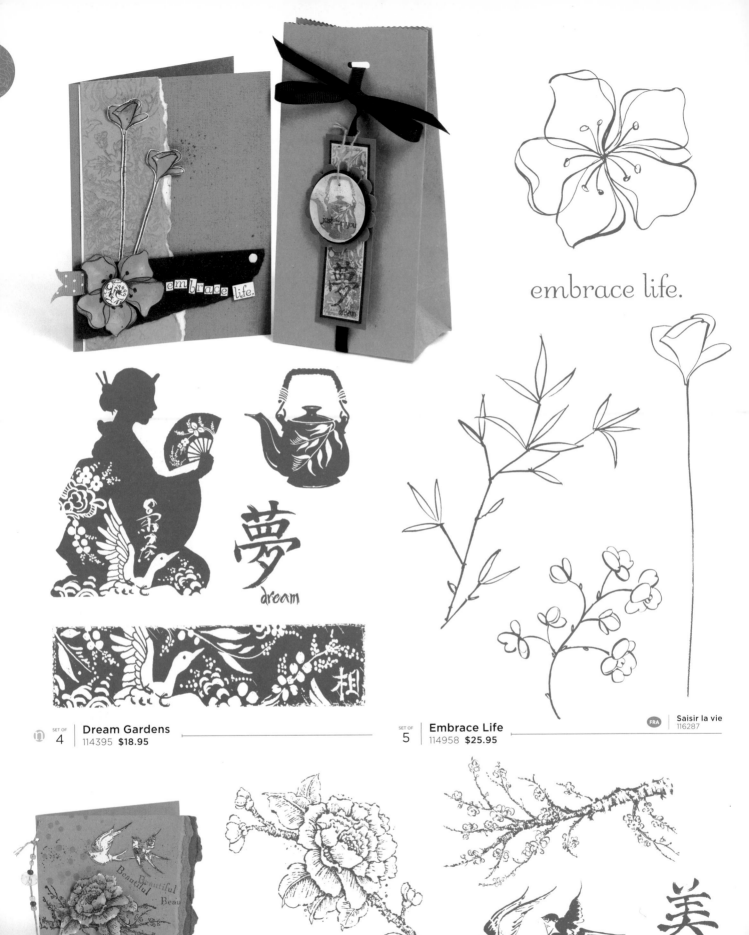

embrace life.

Dream Gardens
SET OF 4 | 114395 **$18.95**

Embrace Life
SET OF 5 | 114958 **$25.95**

FRA | Saisir la vie
116287

夢
dream

美
Beautiful

Eastern Influences
SET OF 4 | 111628 **$18.95**

A true friend reaches for your hand
and touches your heart.

Simple Friendship | SET OF 7
113397 **$25.95**

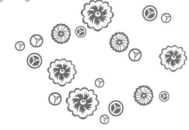

Bird on a Branch | SET OF 5
113266 **$18.95**

Sweet Serenity*
113835 **$6.50**

it's a match

Create matchboxes with ease using our Matchbox Bigz XL die. This die and our Designer Series papers are a perfect match!

Cottage Wall Designer Series Paper
115671 **$9.95** *page 160*

Stampin' Up! Matchbox Bigz XL Die
114890 **$42.95** *page 201*

| SET OF 6 | **A Beautiful Thing** 113618 **$20.95** | | FRA | **Une pure merveille** 113614 |

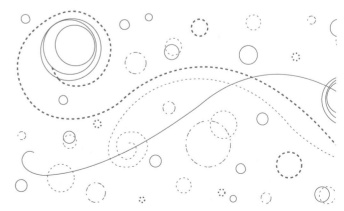

It's Beautiful
111201 **$8.50** *(jumbo)*

Whimsy
109688 **$8.50** *(jumbo)*

Use our Fresh Cuts images with the Fresh-Cut Notes (page 168). The background image overlays the cut-out flower portion to create a beautiful focal point. It can also be used behind the cutout for added versatility.

You're a *friend* who makes good times great.

for you

Gran amiga | ESP
115423

Great Friend | SET OF 5
113792 **$17.95**

enjoy

Thank you

for you

Fraicheur exuise | FRA
114645

Fresh Cuts | SET OF 5
111634 **$21.95**

ALL NATURAL

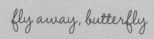

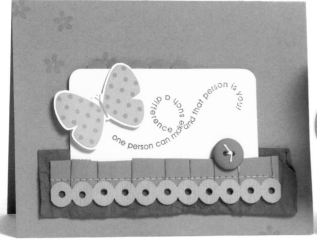

fly away, butterfly

With our Butterfly punch, you can create quick accents that fly right off the project.

Butterfly Punch
116629 **$15.95** page 186

also used on these pages…

Soft Suede Patterns Designer Series Paper
115688 **$9.95** page 161

Chit Chat Rub-Ons
111804 **$10.95** page 177

one person can make and that person is you!

hope your day is as happy as happy gets!

thank you so very much

if nothing ever changed there would be no butterflies. ~unknown

SET OF **10** | **Flight of the Butterfly**
111564 **$31.95**

ESP **Vuelo de la mariposa**
112911

FRA **Sur les ailes d'un papillon**
111752

SET OF **5** | **Eastern Blooms**
111626 **$21.95**

Decorate scalloped edges by adding a small hole to each scallop with the paper-piercing tool.

best friends listen to what you don't say

the time to be happy is now. the place to be happy is here.

Garden Whimsy SET OF 8
113502 **$26.95**

Forest Friends SET OF 4
113748 **$14.95**

Perfect Fit
111251 **$6.50**

ALL NATURAL

HI THERE

GOD writes the GOSPEL
not in the BIBLE alone, but
on TREES and FLOWERS
and CLOUDS and STARS.
~ Martin Luther

SET OF 6 | **Lovely As a Tree**
115026 **$27.95**

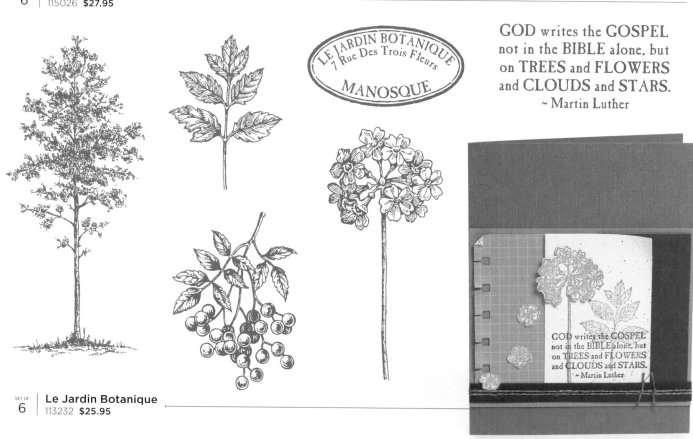

LE JARDIN BOTANIQUE
7 Rue Des Trois Fleurs

MANOSQUE

GOD writes the GOSPEL
not in the BIBLE alone, but
on TREES and FLOWERS
and CLOUDS and STARS.
~ Martin Luther

SET OF 6 | **Le Jardin Botanique**
113232 **$25.95**

Create layers with card stock and ribbon. Add more interest by stamping an image several times and layering each image for a card full of love and full of life!

Live full of love,
Love full of life.

Hojas de vida ESP
116462

Leaf Lines SET OF 6
114393 **$20.95**

Nature's Nest SET OF 5
113826 **$22.95**

good ••••• friend

thinking of you

thanks so much

a special note of thanks

hello there!

you've got a friend in me!

Cheep Talk
113204 **$26.95** | SET OF 11

Petal Pizzazz
113417 **$32.95** | SET OF 7

To add dimension and interest, try stamping the second image on a separate piece of card stock. Then cut it out and adhere using Stampin' Dimensionals.

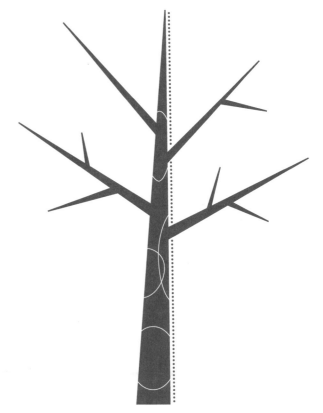

The season of friendship lasts forever.

SET OF **6** | **Season of Friendship**
111776 **$23.95**

SET OF **5** | **Hello Again**
113780 **$12.95**

ESP **Hola de nuevo** 116744   FRA **Salut à toi** 116710

Retro Remix
115619 **$6.50**

elements

I ♥ LISTS

○ ETC.

INGREDIENTS

ODDS & ENDS

THINGS TO BUY

○ ....

○ -

○ ....

○ -

○ ....

○ -

JAN FEB MAR APR MAY JUN JUL AUG SEP OCT NOV DEC

1   2   3   4   5   6   7   8   9   10   11   12   13   14   15   16   17

18   19   20   21   22   23   24   25   26   27   28   29   30   31

SET OF 10 | **I Heart Lists** 116473 **$28.95**

organization

COLLECTION

➱ JUST A
few
OF MY *favorite*
THINGS
0123456789

Whether you're an expert organizer or organization just isn't your thing, you'll find something to love in our selection of organizational products. Best of all, it's designed to coordinate.

try this technique...

1.

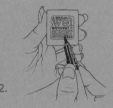

2.

1. Create a multicolored image by coloring directly on the stamp with a marker. **2.** Fill in the rest of the image with another marker.

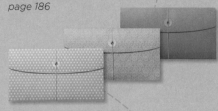

**Modern Label
Punch**
116630 **$15.95**
page 186

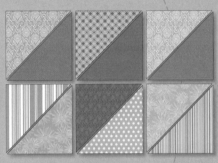

**Thoroughly Modern
Designer Gusseted Envelopes**
115693 **$5.95**
page 169

**Thoroughly Modern
Designer Series Paper**
115673 **$9.95**
page 163

**Thoroughly Modern
Designer File Folders**
115692 **$10.95**
page 169

it's **all** in the **details**

FOR...
☐ TODAY
☐ TOMORROW
☐ ANOTHER DAY
☐ NEVER

➱ JUST A
few
OF MY *favorite*
THINGS
0123456789

Favorite Things   SET OF
115436 **$23.95**   **5**

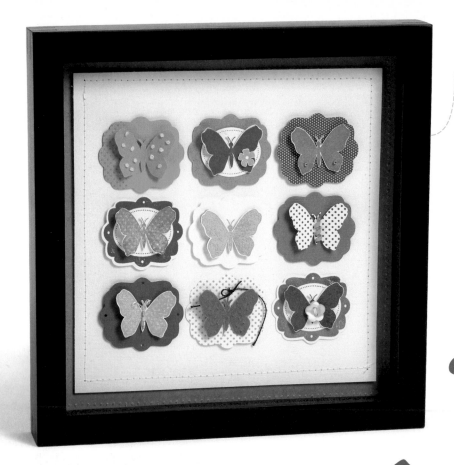

Use the For All You Do set with the Delicate Dots wheel (page 65) for beautifully coordinated creations.

thank you

{ for all you do, for all you are, for all you mean to me…

For All You Do
SET OF 10 | 115360 **$28.95**

ESP | **Por todo lo que haces** 116742   FRA | **Merci pour tout** 116708

HELLO

Pendant Park
SET OF 4 | 115456 **$23.95**

ESP | **Un dia en el parque** 116845   FRA | **Adorable parc** 116843

Use our Matchbox die and coordinating Matchbox Messages set to create labels for tags, cards, and other projects.

find *joy* in the *little* things

a little something

Framed with Love | SET OF 7
114389 $27.95

Celebrate

♥
a little something

Sweet One

just a little thanks

Matchbox Messages | SET OF 6
113800 $25.95

SET OF
11 | **Pick a Petal**
115042 **$29.95**

SET OF
4 | **Stem Sayings**
115078 **$20.95**

FRA | **Phrases précieuses**
116271

SET OF
6 | **Little Flowers**
115020 **$11.95**

Little Bits
109691 **$6.50**

You're one of the GOOD ones!

QUEEN OF EVERYTHING

Happy birthday

J · YOU MAKE ME LAUGH

K · KING FOR A DAY

Q · QUEEN OF EVERYTHING

Card Games | SET OF
113202 **$19.95** | 3

BIG WINNER!

game night

JACKPOT

Game Night | SET OF
113220 **$20.95** | 8

game night

JACKPOT

game night

In the Cards
113831 **$6.50**

ELEMENTS   **121**

SET OF 8 | **Wanted**
115106 **$23.95**

A *true* FRIEND IS **YOU** FRIEND

| Amitié sincère
112644

SET OF 6 | **True Friend**
110378 **$22.95**

 | **Boho Friend**
110334 **$6.50**

window to the world

Create card accents quickly with our Punch Windows Magnetic Movers & Shapers and add perfect layers with our coordinating punches. The window makes placement easy!

Stampin' Up! Punch Windows Magnetic Movers & Shapers
115953 **$29.95** *page 201*

Large Star Punch
110710 **$15.95** *page 186*

WONDERFUL FRIEND

TYLER

Just saying hello!

Seeing Stars | SET OF 8
115352 **$21.95**

WONDERFUL FRIEND

YOU MAKE ME HAPPY

Motifs bohémians FRA
116299

Boho Backgrounds | SET OF 4
114940 **$17.95**

ELEMENTS **123**

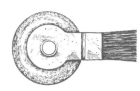

sorry about that

grateful
for you

hope you
perk up
soon

sew glad we're
friends

just my type

picture
perfect

rubber baby
buggy bumpers

fan mail

SET OF
8 | **Puns from the Past**
111676 **$27.95**

Learn
from yesterday,
Live
for today,
Hope
for tomorrow.

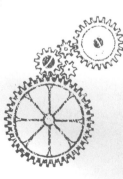

An *unhurried* sense of time
is in itself a form of *wealth*.
~BONNIE FRIEDMAN

SET OF
4 | **Sense of Time**
113804 **$22.95**

Use our watercoloring tools to create a perfect masterpiece like the Cello card below. You'll find blender pens and Aqua Painters on page 192.

Music expresses that which cannot be said.
~Victor Hugo

Music Expressions | SET OF 2
113718 **$16.95**

Symphony
(jumbo) 113832 **$8.50**

thank you

JUST FOR **YOU**

fabulous FRIEND

Todos ovalados | ESP | En ovale | FRA
115425 | | 114649

 Oval All | SET OF 4
113790 **$16.95**

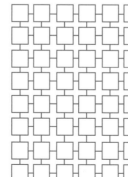

You can use circle punches for all kinds of projects. Punch out a full circle image, then using a smaller circle, punch part of an image and layer for a unique three-dimensional look.

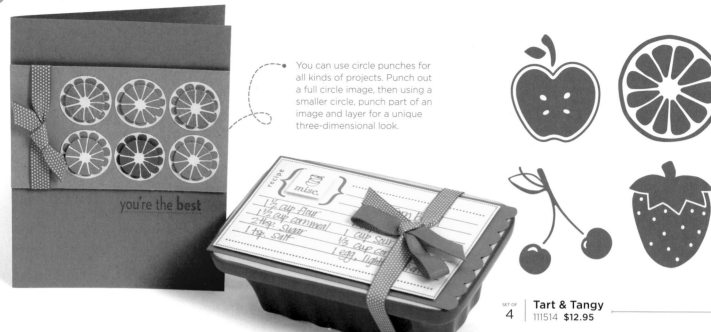

you're the best

SET OF 4 | **Tart & Tangy**
111514 **$12.95**

desserts   misc.

veggies, salads **& sides**   meats **&** **main** dishes

breads   **soups,** stews **&** sauces

yum **scale**
☆ ☆ ☆ ☆ ☆   from the **kitchen** of:

recipe { }

SET OF 9 | **From the Kitchen of**
114964 **$29.95**

SET OF 4 | **Park Avenue Patterns**
114445 **$19.95**

Gallery
113776 **$22.95** | SET OF 3

menu

Grapefruit, Jicama, & Avocado Salad

Braised Chicken with Mushrooms

Brown Butter Mashed Potatoes

Chocolate Mocha Mousse

menu

{bon appétit}

you're invited

compliments to the chef

Compliments to the Chef
114397 **$20.95** | SET OF 6

Felicitaciones por la exquisita cena
116740 ESP

Mes compliments au chef
116706 FRA

ELEMENTS 127

All the stamp sets on pages 128–129 coordinate with our punches (page 186).

TOP SECRET

bona fide

IMPORTANT

SET OF
6 | **Certified**
113706 **$27.95**

HAPPY BIRTHDAY

SET OF
4 | **Four Square**
111632 **$14.95**

THANKS

SET OF
4 | **Only Ovals**
111666 **$22.95**

texturize

Our Texturz plates (page 195) create subtle and beautiful backgrounds. For best results, lightly spray your paper or card stock with water before using the plate.

Stampin' Up! Backgrounds 1 Texturz Plates
114512 **$11.95** *page 195*

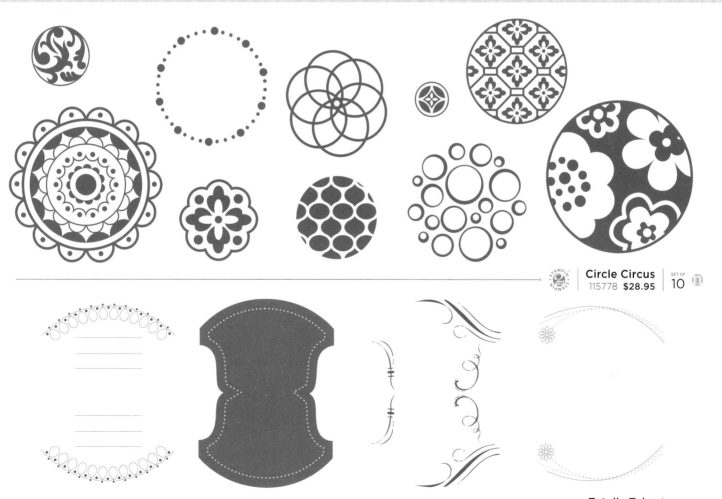

Circle Circus
115778 **$28.95** SET OF 10

Totally Tabs
113520 **$17.95** SET OF 4

PRICELESS

SO*KIND

SET OF 11 | **Priceless**
115052 **$28.95**

for you

{ YOU ARE *One*
OF A KIND }

SET OF 6 | **One of a Kind**
113624 **$19.95**

FRA Unique en ton genre
113556

Make quick treat or gift baskets with our Baskets & Blooms Bigz XL die (page 200).

HELLO

lacey

cherish

kind

Motifs baroques
113544   FRA

Baroque Motifs   SET OF
113490 **$27.95**   6

Baroque Border
109675 **$6.50**

May every part of your BIRTHDAY have **happy** in it!

hope happens.

BIG DAY!

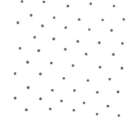

Itty Bitty Backgrounds
SET OF 4 · 114996 **$14.95**

Sprinkles
SET OF 4 · 115076 **$14.95**

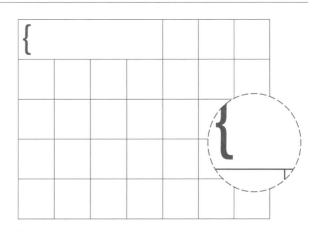

PRACTICE

GAME

REMEMBER

BIG DAY!

@

Cute Cues
SET OF 6 · 111622 **$11.95**

Calendar*
SET OF 1 · 109298 **$17.95**

*THIS BACKGROUND STAMP IS SHOWN AT 45% WITH A SMALL PORTION OF THE IMAGE SHOWN AT ACTUAL SIZE.

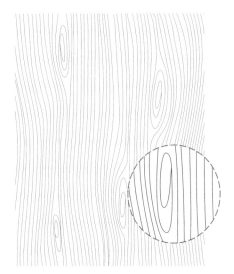

Approximate dimensions for all background stamps are 4-1/2" x 5-3/4". The Medallion stamp is shown at actual size. All other background stamps show the full image at 45%, with a small portion of the image at actual size.

 Medallion
115223 **$17.95** | SET OF 1

 Classifieds
111616 **$17.95** | SET OF 1

 French Filigree
113742 **$17.95** | SET OF 1

Woodgrain
117100 **$17.95** | SET OF 1

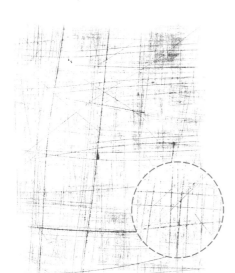

SET OF 1 **Sanded**
109294 **$17.95**

SET OF 1 **Pretty Petals**
111008 **$17.95**

SET OF 1 **Gratuitous Graffiti**
111636 **$17.95**

SET OF 1 **Très Chic**
109258 **$17.95**

SET OF 1 **Bella Toile**
111598 **$17.95**

SET OF 1 **En Français**
109521 **$17.95**

SET OF 2 **It's a Plan**
111658 **$26.95** *(double-mounted)*

FRA **Planifions**
112877

SET OF 1 **Boho Blooms**
111608 **$17.95**

greetings

personalized stamps

Stamp your personal belongings and correspondence with Stampin' Up!'s personalized stamps. Choose from 11 designs to create a stamp that meets your needs.

hand stamped by

The "Hand Stamped By" personalized name stamps below fulfill the requirements of Stampin' Up!'s Angel Policy, which governs the sale of hand-stamped items. For more information, contact your demonstrator or go to www.stampinup.com.

Personalized name stamps must be ordered using special forms. Ask your demonstrator for assistance. Please note: No returns can be accepted on personalized name stamps.

"Hand Stamped By" Stamp

One line of personalized text (for name), up to 16 characters. Spaces count as a character; capitals count as 2 spaces. Fulfills Stampin' Up!'s Angel Policy.

115602 Butterfly	$18.95

hand stamped by
Your Name Here
© STAMPIN' UP!

"Hand Stamped By" Stamp

One line of personalized text (for name), up to 16 characters. Spaces count as a character; capitals count as 2 spaces. Fulfills Stampin' Up!'s Angel Policy.

115600 Flourish	$18.95

hand stamped by
Your Name Here
© STAMPIN' UP!

Text-Only Stamp

Choose from 1-4 lines of text, up to 32 characters per line. Spaces count as a character; capitals count as 2 spaces.

115576	Conventional One-Line	$10.95
115578	Conventional Two-Line	$13.95
115580	Conventional Three-Line	$15.95
115582	Conventional Four-Line	$17.95

FIRST & LAST NAME
1234 Your Street
City, State 12345
(123) 456-7890

Text-Only Stamp

Choose from 1-4 lines of text, up to 32 characters per line. Spaces count as a character; capitals count as 2 spaces.

115584	Tailored One-Line	$10.95
115586	Tailored Two-Line	$13.95
115588	Tailored Three-Line	$15.95
115590	Tailored Four-Line	$17.95

First & Last Name
1234 Your Street
City, State 12345
(123) 456-7890

Text-and-Image Stamp

Choose from 1-4 lines of text, up to 32 characters per line. Spaces count as a character; capitals count as 2 spaces. Font styles and images cannot be interchanged.

116632	Family Tree One-Line	$14.95
116633	Family Tree Two-Line	$16.95
116634	Family Tree Three-Line	$18.95
116635	Family Tree Four-Line	$20.95

First & Last Name
1234 Your Street
City, State 12345
(123) 456-7890

Text-and-Image Stamp

Choose from 1-4 lines of text, up to 32 characters per line. Spaces count as a character; capitals count as 2 spaces. Font styles and images cannot be interchanged.

116636	Home One-Line	$14.95
116637	Home Two-Line	$16.95
116638	Home Three-Line	$18.95
116639	Home Four-Line	$20.95

First & Last Name
1234 Your Street
City, State 12345
(123) 456-7890

Pirate Personalized Name Stamp

One line of personalized text (for name), up to 26 characters. Spaces count as a character; capitals count as 2 spaces. The word "Captain" counts towards the 26 characters and must be entered on the personalized name stamp form if you wish for it to be included in front of your child's name.

115524	Captain	$9.95

Captain Levi Hansen

Princess Personalized Name Stamp

One line of personalized text (for name), up to 26 characters. Spaces count as a character; capitals count as 2 spaces. The word "Princess" counts towards the 26 characters and must be entered on the personalized name stamp form if you wish for it to be included in front of your child's name.

115525	Princess	$9.95

PRINCESS ANNA FOXLEY

Wedding Personalized Stamp

One line of personalized text (date), up to 16 characters. Spaces count as a character; capitals count as 2 spaces.

116480	Special Date	$10.95

12.08.2010

Wedding Personalized Stamp

Choose up to 3 lines of text (for name, in all caps), up to 26 characters per line. Spaces count as a character.

115464	Yours and Mine	$15.95

EMMA MARIE HARRISON
AND
MICHAEL ALEX ROBINSON

Large Text-Only Stamps

Choose either 1 or 2 lines of text, up to 16 characters per line. Spaces count as a character; capitals count as 2 spaces.

115596	Basic One-Line	$13.95
115598	Basic Two-Line	$15.95

Name Here
(123) 456-7890

TO MY   HELLO

THANKS   FRIEND

SO SORRY   LOVE

WISHES   FAMILY

WITH JOY   HAPPY

XOXOXO   PARTY

EVERYTHING   CELEBRATE   CONGRATS   HI THERE

ANNIVERSARY   GOOD LUCK   FOR YOU   MR. & MRS.

BIRTHDAY   CHRISTMAS   FOREVER   NEW BABY

| SET OF 24 | **Fundamental Phrases** 114968 **$37.95** (double-mounted) | | ESP | Frases bàsicas 112917 | FRA | Les mots pour le dire 116255 |

CELEBRATE **YOU**

HAPPY BIRTHDAY
...and you thought I forgot

{ make a wish }

| SET OF 4 | **A Little Birthday Cheer** 115018 **$13.95** | | FRA | Un petit plaisir de fête 112650 |

Things have been rough between us.
I just want to say I'm sorry.

You know that thing I said?
I wish I hadn't. I'm sorry.

I've never known someone so brave.
I'm praying for you.

You are stronger than this.
You are brave and courageous.
And let's face it.
You're my friend, so that means
you can put up with anything.

Sometimes the only thing making
life's darkest moments bearable
is having someone by your side
reminding you that it will be okay.

**Thank you for being
that kind of friend.**

Life doesn't always happen just as we planned,
but I plan to be there for you always.

| SET OF 6 | **Hard to Say** 115419 **$23.95** |

I've never known someone so brave.
I'm praying for you.

i love you

i miss you

you, you, you

so very sorry

thanks so much

thinking of you

 hree little words...

Three Little Words | SET OF 8
(double-mounted) 113254 **$13.95**

on your
BIRTHDAY...

*Just thinking of you
on your birthday!*

Happy Birthday!

It's your day...
ENJOY!

birthday
GREETINGS

wishing you the
HAPPIEST
birthday yet!

let's
celebrate!

(A little **late!**)

look who's
turning

( )

I just wanted to give you
a reason to celebrate
a **little** longer!
Happy Belated Birthday

happy o' birthday

LIVE, LAUGH
& LOVE
happy birthday

Pour ton anniversaire
111724 FRA

On Your Birthday | SET OF 12
111664 **$33.95**

punch a bunch

Emphasize a greeting by
framing it using one of our
punches, such as the Scallop
Oval punch used here.

♡ Scallop Oval Punch
114889 **$15.95** *page 186*

also used on these pages...

Fleurettes II
Accents & Elements
115604 **$9.95** *page 180*

GREETINGS

buttons, brads, and bows

When it comes to giving your project the finishing touch, look no further than our embellishments, such as buttons, brads, and bows.

Melon Mambo
1/2" Polka-Dot Grosgrain Ribbon
115611 **$9.95** *page 182*

Pretties Kit
109114 **$29.95** *page 178*

Clear Rhinestone Brads
113144 **$10.95** *page 179*

I'm here for you always... please know that I care.

Sending you a little something wrapped in a whole lot of love!

One little baby... many happy hearts!

If wishes could make you well... you'd be better already!

Wishing you love and laughter forever after!

You're a wonderful reason to celebrate!

Time passes... friendship stays right where it's put!

Two simple words that come with so much gratitude...thank you.

SET OF 8 | **Curvy Verses**
114948 **$23.95**

FRA | Vagues d'émotions
116277

A friend is someone who strengthens you with prayers, blesses you with love, and encourages you with hope.

May the God of love be the heart of your marriage, the light of your home, and the ever-present partner in your new life together.

Sharing with you the miracle of new hope and new life through the glorious gift of Christ the Lord.

Today is God's gift to you ... Each day you are God's gift to me!

HAPPY BIRTHDAY

May God's love heal your sorrow, and may His peace replace your heartache with warm and loving memories.

Blessings brighten when we count them!

THANK YOU for blessing my life in such a wonderful way!

May the miracle of Christmas find you safe in the Peace of God, warm in the Light of Christ.

A baby is a gift from heaven above— bringing joy down to earth, filling hearts full of love.

SET OF 8 | **God's Blessings**
114972 **$33.95**

Plant your feet firmly and
let your heart have wings.

Whoever is happy will make
others happy too. ~Anne Frank

hope happens.

It takes COURAGE
to grow up
and become who you
REALLY are.

Do not put off till
TOMORROW
what can be
Enjoyed
TODAY.

~Josh Billings

hope happens.

Welcome baby

Hope Happens
113722 **$19.95** | SET OF 5

best wishes • wish big • love you
thank you • Welcome baby • very merry

Short & Sweet
115060 **$17.95** | SET OF 12

happiness • adorable • Welcome • cherish
sparkle • be merry • Wonderful • giggle

Warm Words
115108 **$21.95** | SET OF 8

ONCE UPON A TIME...

...and they lived
happily ever after...

FAIRY TALES
DO COME TRUE...

the end

SWEET
adorable
friend

Once Upon a Time
113746 **$19.95** | SET OF 4

GREETINGS 141

FOR YOU   TOGETHER   DAYS

BIRTHDAY   HOLIDAYS   LIFE

happy
EVERYTHING

SET OF 8 | **Happy Everything**
115235 **$18.95**

FRA Joyeux Joyeux
116249

kindness

comes in many forms but always from the heart.

welcome *christmas* into your heart.

may all your *wishes* come true!

wishing you *happiness* today & always.

SET OF 4 | **Heard from the Heart**
111644 **$22.95**

FRA Tout droit du cœur
112875

Wonderful favorite

husband	grand	and	to my	brother	step	cousin
daughter	friend	aunt	sister	mother	to a	-in-law
nephew	niece	son	uncle	couple	wife	father

SET OF 23 | **Wonderful Favorites**
115114 **$40.95**

What if the HOKEY POKEY really is
what it's ALL about?

BE YOURSELF.

Nobody is better qualified!

You're never too old
to do GOOFY stuff.

~Ward Cleaver

You're one of the
GOOD ones!

• • • • • • • • • • •

If at first you don't succeed,
find out
if the loser gets anything.

~Bill Lyon

FRIEND. GOOD.
FRIEND. GOOD.
FRIEND. GOOD.
FRIEND. GOOD.
—Frankenstein

Time is no longer money.
HAPPY RETIREMENT.

FRIEND. GOOD.
—Frankenstein

Smarty Pants
115070 **$18.95** | SET OF | 6

Let the FUN begin!

Time is no longer money.
HAPPY RETIREMENT.

I hear _____
is the new _____.

Hey there,
grandma

Opportunity
knocked,
and YOU
answered.

Hey there,
grandpa

Let the Fun Begin | SET OF | 6
115350 **$17.95**

YOU'RE
Invited   *Thinking*
OF YOU

BEST
wishes   *so much*   *Get well*
THANKS   SOON

Birthday   *Good*   *Greetings*
WISHES   LUCK   HOLIDAY

Sincères salutations   FRA
116239

Sincere Salutations | SET OF | 8
115068 **$23.95**

Use our exclusive Stampin' Up! Sizzlits dies (page 196) to make your cards unique. The Celebrate card below uses the Floral Fusion die with vellum.

FYI

you make me smile.	i miss you.	it will get better.
today is your birthday.	i'm expecting!	i owe you big time.
i'm so happy for you!	i care.	you are awesome.
i'm really sorry.		

SET OF 11 | **FYI** 114365 **$19.95**

THANK YOU

celebrate

GOOD TIMES   FRIENDSHIP   YOUR DAY

TIME TO   TODAY   LIFE   YOU

SET OF 1 | **Elegant Thank You** 114484 **$6.95**
ESP Gracias 114552   **FRA** Merci bien 114504

SET OF 8 | **Celebrate Everything** 114942 **$18.95**
FRA Tout célébrer 116281

SET OF 6 | **Think Happy Thoughts** 115092 **$16.95**

FRA Des pensées positives 116263

TO HAVE
&
TO HOLD
...
FOREVER
&
ALWAYS

celebrate
make a wish
EAT CAKE
live for the presents
PARTY HEARTY
(IT'S YOUR DAY!)

SUGAR
and
SPICE
and
EVERYTHING
NICE

SNIPS
AND
SNAILS
AND
PUPPYDOG
TAILS

Everything Nice
113818 **$17.95** | SET OF 4

happy new year!

i'm so sorry

for your shower

happy
st. patrick's day

Happy Retirement

sweet treats

MERRY CHRISTMAS

happy birthday

Happy Anniversary

just for you

HAPPY GRADUATION

hello baby

happy valentine's day

thank you

HAPPY THANKSGIVING

Happy Easter

For the Newlyweds

With Sympathy

happy mother's day

thinking of you

happy halloween

get well wishes

HAPPY FATHER'S DAY

{friend to friend}

Deseos pequeñitos
116841 ESP | Vœux mignons
117989 FRA

Teeny Tiny Wishes
115370 **$36.95** | SET OF 24

Thank You

Kind Thanks

thanks

A NOTE OF THANKS

Tous mes remerciements
111742 FRA

Thank You Kindly
111700 **$13.95** | SET OF 4

GREETINGS **145**

party for

_____

date

_____

place

_____

11 12 1
10 · 2
9 · 3
8 · 4
7 6 5

surprise ☐

_____

host

_____

rsvp

Celebrate!

In Honor of:

Date:

Time:

Place:

Registered:

You're Invited!

For

When

At

Save the Date

JOIN US FOR THE CELEBRATION

EVENT

DATE

LOCATION

PLEASE COME

SET OF 5 | **Please Come**
115046 **$25.95**

limited edition

Created by:

© STAMPIN' UP!

HANDMADE · HANDMADE
HANDMADE · HANDMADE

┌─────────────────┐
│ PHOTOGRAPH BY │
│ №   │
└─────────────────┘

HAND STAMPED
© STAMPIN' UP!

art

MADE WITH LOVE
© STAMPIN' UP!

{ *original design* }

ESP Arte y Diseño
112891

FRA Art & Design
116265

SET OF 8 | **Art by Design**
114920 **$17.95**

SAVE THE DATE

INTRODUCING...

you're INVITED

FOR

DATE

TIME

PLACE

RSVP

SET OF 4 | **Introducing**
114443 **$15.95**

SAVE THE DATE

for the wedding of Kate & Benjamin
October Third, Two Thousand and Nine
New York City, New York

May every part
of your BIRTHDAY
have **happy** in it!

Once in a while,
RIGHT IN THE MIDDLE
of
an ORDINARY life,
Love gives us a
FAIRYTALE.

Life
is what HAPPENS to you
while you're BUSY
making **other plans**.
~John Lennon

A BEST FRIEND
is someone who
brings out the BEST in YOU.

May every part
of your BIRTHDAY
have **happy** in it!

If at FIRST you **do** succeed,
try *not* to look ASTONISHED.

Thanks . . . not just
for the BIG things you do,
but all the **wonderful**
little things too!

a new HAND to hold,
a new heart to LOVE,
a new LIFE to lead.

Full of Life | SET OF
111500 **$28.95** | 7

THANKS
your order is appreciated
your order is appreciated

new!

PLEASE
come

GIRLS'
NIGHT
OUT

{ A *Fabulous*
GIFT FOR YOU }

❋ wish list ❋

Thank You
for your order

limited

TO DO:
☐
☐
☐
☐
☐

Phone me
to place an order

Special

Phone me
to place an order

Andrea Bowden
Independent Demonstrator

(800) 782-6787
www.andrea.stampinup.net

Taking Care of Business | SET OF
115090 **$25.95** | 11

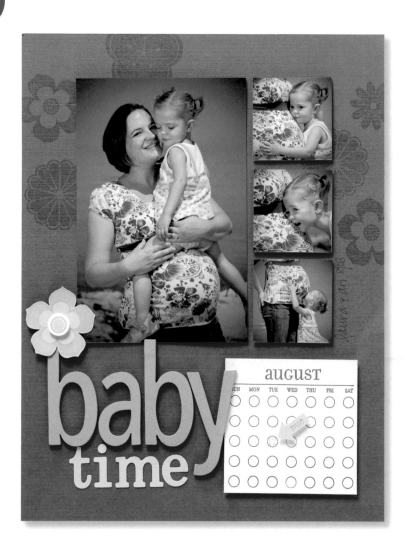

HAPPY BIRTHDAY   SAVE THE DATE

IT'S A PARTY   DUE DATE   YOU'RE INVITED

SUN	MON	TUE	WED	THU	FRI	SAT
○	○	○	○	○	○	○
○	○	○	○	○	○	○
○	○	○	○	○	○	○
○	○	○	○	○	○	○
○	○	○	○	○	○	○

✓   DUE   ♥   ●

SET OF 13 · **Mark the Date** · 115034 **$26.95**

january   july
february   august
march   september
april   october
may   november
june   december

SET OF 12 | **Full Calendar**
114966 **$17.95** (double-mounted)

alphabets

Create your own tags, scrapbook titles, framed pictures, and more with our alphabets, available in many styles and sizes.

also used on these pages...

Old Olive
1-1/4" Striped Grosgrain Ribbon
115618 **$8.95** *page 183*

Heart to Heart Punch
113694 **$15.95** *page 186*

The Write Stuff
Specialty Designer Series Paper
115674 **$11.95** *page 163*

Varsity Alphabet
(double-mounted) 113684 **$43.95** | SET OF 26

Taffy Alphabet
(double-mounted) 115086 **$43.95** | SET OF 28

Varsity Numbers
(double-mounted) 113686 **$24.95** | SET OF 12

Taffy Numbers
(double-mounted) 115088 **$24.95** | SET OF 12

Jumble Alphabet

aA BbCc dD Ee Ff 9g
Hh *i*i jJ Kk Ll Mm Nn
Oo Pp Qq Rr Ss tt Uu
Vv Ww Xx Yy Zz

ACTUAL SIZE | FULL SET SHOWN AT 40%

SET OF 52 | **Jumble Alphabet**
115199 **$43.95** *(double-mounted)*

Defining Alphabet

Aa Bb Cc Dd Ee Ff
Gg Hh Ii Jj Kk Ll
Mm Nn Oo Pp Qq Rr
Ss Tt Uu Vv Ww Xx
Yy Zz a *little* LETTER *for you!*

ACTUAL SIZE | FULL SET SHOWN AT 40%

SET OF 28 | **Defining Alphabet**
114952 **$43.95** *(double-mounted)*

---

al•ways : {ôl′wāz} *adv.*
Every minute of every day. Forever; unchanging. At all times; invariably.

ACTUAL SIZE | FULL SET SHOWN AT 40%

al•ways : {ôl′wāz} *adv.*
Every minute of every day. Forever; unchanging. At all times; invariably.

be•cause : {bǐ-kôz′} *conj.*
Just because; for a reason; the reason being. *"Because I love you,"* or *"Because you're worth it."*

cre•ate : {krē-āt′} *tr. v.*
To produce through artistic or imaginative effort. Create and inspire. To make your own.

de•light : {dĭ-līt′} *n.*
A high degree of enjoyment. Expressions of joy; extreme satisfaction. *"You are a delight."*

eve•ry•thing : {ĕv′rē-thĭng′} *pron.* All things that are meaningful to you. All that you know; the whole world.

fa•vor•ite : {fā′vər-ĭt′} *n.*
Something regarded with special favor or liking. Best loved; preferred above all others.

grat•i•tude : {grăt′ĭ-tōōd′} *n.*
Cause of happiness or joy. Expressing appreciation for something or someone.

hap•py : {hăp′ē} *adj.*
Cheerful; tickled pink; content. Simple pleasure; together. A feeling of giddiness or joy.

in•spire : {ĭn-spīr′} *v.*
To cause or create new ideas. Fresh thought; to influence. To motivate one to action.

jour•ney : {jûr-nē′} *n.*
An experience or process that leaves you changed; trail of experience. From here to there.

kind•ness : {kīnd′nĭs} *n.*
Goodness for the sake of being good. Warm-hearted and considerate. Acts of kindness.

lu•cky : {lŭk′ē} *adj.*
Fortune smiles upon you. Favored with optimal circumstances. Lucky you; just lucky.

mem•or•ies : {mĕm′ə-rēz} *n.*
Recollection of the past; retaining and recalling experiences. Thoughts of good times past.

near•ly : {nǐr′lē} *adv.*
In a close manner; intimately. Almost but not quite; nearly everything. So very close.

or•i•gin•al : {ə-rĭj′ə-nəl} *adj.*
Fresh and inventive. One of a kind; unique; first in its class. Work of heart. *"Be original."*

per•fect : {pûr′fĭkt} *adj.*
Lacking nothing essential to the whole; giving your best. Flawless; admirable. Just right.

qual•i•ty : {kwŏl′ĭ-tē} *n.*
Well-made or durable. Top of the line; excellent; high class. To provide the best.

re•mem•ber : {rĭ-mĕm′bər} *v.*
To keep in mind as worthy of consideration or recognition. Memories of days gone by.

sim•ple : {sĭm′pəl} *adj.*
Joy in little things; without pretense or show. In a plain or unadorned way; in a snap.

to•geth•er : {tə-gĕth′ər} *adv.*
You and me; lonely no more. With another; inseparable. In harmony; in sync.

u•nique : {yōō-nēk′} *adj.*
Being the only one of its kind. Unusual; extraordinary. Unlike any other; having no equal.

ver•y : {vĕr′ē} *adv.*
To a high degree; extremely; Truly. To emphasize a good quality. *"You are very special."*

wish : {wĭsh} *n.*
Heart's desire; to dream of; reach for; aspire to. To want. *"Wish upon a star."*

x•o•x•o : {ĕks-ō-ĕks-ō} *n.*
Hugs and kisses; love and affection. Closing or salutation of a love note; with love.

you : {yōō} *pron.*
The one and only; the one I value as my friend and love each day. The person in my thoughts.

zeal : {zēl} *n.*
Enthusiastic devotion to a cause, ideal, or goal. Passion; energy; zest for life.

[DEFINE *your* *life!*]

SET OF 28 | **Define Your Life**
114950 **$47.95** *(double-mounted)*

Jumbo Outline Alphabet
(double-mounted) 114998 **$43.95** | SET OF 24

ab&

Schoolbook Serif Alphabet
(double-mounted) 113510 **$43.95** | SET OF 24

123}

Schoolbook Serif Numbers
(double-mounted) 111680 **$24.95** | SET OF 12

a b c d e f g h i j k l m n o p
q r s t v w x y z 1 2 3 4 5 6 7
8 9 10 11 12 13 14 15 16 17 18 19
20 21 22 23 24 25 26 27 28 29 30 31

Calendar Alphabet & Numbers
(double-mounted) 111610 **$20.95** | SET OF 56

The Jumbo Outline and Schoolbook Serif Alphabets include 24 stamps, with "b" used as "q," "d" used as "p," and "n" used as "u" when stamped upside-down. Calendar Alphabet & Numbers uses "n" used as "u" when stamped upside-down. The Taffy Numbers use the "6" as "9" when stamped upside-down.

a b c d e f

Just Perfect Alphabet
(double-mounted) 115358 **$19.95** | SET OF 26

A B —··— &

Monogram Sweet
115462 **$31.95** | SET OF 28

a b c
& and
no.

123456789
012345678
901234567
890123456
789012345

Contempo Alphabet
(double-mounted) 111570 **$43.95** | SET OF 30

When you assemble the stamps in the mini alphabet sets, two stamps go on each wood block, with one at each end. Put the clear label on the blocks first to guide you when positioning the stamps.

Bb 1 Baby	**We** 2 Wedding	**Bd** 3 Birthday
Tm 4 Thanks much	**Sh** 5 Surprise!	**Co** 6 Congrats!
Hi 7 & Hello	**Ch** 8 Cheers	**Ha** 9 Happy
Jn 10 Jingle	**Xo** 11 Hugs & Kisses	**Ce** 12 Celebrate

Perfect Chemistry
114383 **$21.95** | SET OF 12

A B C D

ABCDEFGHI
JKLMNOPQR
STUVWXYZ

ACTUAL SIZE | FULL SET SHOWN AT 50%

SET OF **26** | **Jayne's Type Alphabet**
114401 **$43.95** *(double-mounted)*

ABCDEFGHIJ
KLMNOPQRST
UVWXYZ *2?* ❦ *and* &

ACTUAL SIZE | FULL SET SHOWN AT 50%

SET OF **30** | **Lovely Letters Alphabet**
115030 **$43.95** *(double-mounted)*

A B C D E F G H I J
K L M N O P Q R S T
U V W X Y Z ! & ★ ❧

ACTUAL SIZE | FULL SET SHOWN AT 50%

SET OF **30** | **Wild West Alphabet**
115112 **$43.95** *(double-mounted)*

accessories

Whether you have a color scheme in mind or want to see our complete line of colors, you're in the right place! The next four pages list several of the products you can purchase in our exclusive colors.

color coordination

Stampin' Write Markers

Set of 48 Stampin' Write dual-tip markers. These markers feature a fine tip for details and writing and a brush tip for wider applications. Each marker is like getting 2 long-lasting markers in 1. Horizontal storage case keeps both tips inked evenly.

105541	Many Marvelous Markers	**$125.95**
105538	Bold Brights (12)	**$31.95**
105539	Earth Elements (12)	**$31.95**
105540	Rich Regals (12)	**$31.95**
105537	Soft Subtles (12)	**$31.95**
109126	Neutrals (4)**	**$10.95**

Stampin' Pastels

Enjoy artist-quality, blendable pastels in Stampin' Up!'s exclusive colors. Protected in a sturdy case complete with color guide inside lid. Includes 6 applicators and an eraser.

105542	Stampin' Pastels®	**$24.95**

Watercolor Pencils

Made with deep pigments, our brilliantly colored pencils come in a sturdy tin container. Use alone to color stamped images or use with a blender pen, watercolor brushes or Aqua Painter for lovely effects. Acid free. 24 assorted colors. *sm*

101879	Watercolor Pencils	**$19.95**

Watercolor Wonder™ Crayons

Water-soluble and easy-to-blend crayons in Stampin' Up!'s exclusive colors allow for an almost unlimited range of shades. Use with a blender pen or Aqua Painter for stunning results. Watercolor Wonder Crayons are perfect with the Aqua Painter. *sm*

106695	Bold Brights (12)	**$19.95**
106696	Earth Elements (12)	**$19.95**
106698	Rich Regals (12)	**$19.95**
106697	Soft Subtles (12)	**$19.95**
106746	Neutrals (6)	**$9.95**

in color

in color	Classic stampin' pad $5.95	Classic ink refill $2.95	markers stampin' write	card stock 8-1/2" x 11" (24 sheets) $5.50	card stock 8-1/2" x 11" textured	card stock 12" x 12"	card stock 12" x 12" textured	ribbon polka-dot grosgrain $9.95
RICH RAZZLEBERRY	115658	115664	–	115316	–	–	–	115613
MELON MAMBO	115656	115662	–	115320	–	–	–	115611
CRUSHED CURRY	115659	115665	–	115319	–	–	–	115614
DUSTY DURANGO	115654	115660	–	115321	–	–	–	115609
BERMUDA BAY	115655	115661	–	115317	–	–	–	115610
SOFT SUEDE	115657	115663	–	115318	–	–	–	115612
assorted			(set of 6) $17.95	36 sheets (6 ea. of 6 colors) $7.95	36 sheets (6 ea. of 6 colors) $10.95	24 sheets (4 ea. of 6 colors) $8.95	24 sheets (4 ea. of 6 colors) $11.95	
IN COLOR	–	–	116329	115315	115719	115314	115538	

neutrals

neutrals	Classic stampin' pad $5.95	Classic ink refill $2.95	markers stampin' write $3.25	Craft stampin' pad $7.50	Craft ink refill $4.25	card stock 8-1/2" x 11" (40 sheets) $7.50	card stock 12" x 12" (20 sheets) $7.50	card stock 12" x 12" textured	cartridges standard cartridge $5.25	cartridges jumbo cartridge $7.50
WHISPER WHITE	–	–	–	101731	101780	100730	106529	–	–	–
VERY VANILLA	–	–	–	104308	104328	101650	106530	–	–	–
SAHARA SAND	105208	105220	105105	–	–	105328	106531	–	–	–
BASIC BROWN	104315*	104314*	–	–	–	–	–	–	–	–
GOING GRAY	103274	102521	–	–	–	–	–	–	–	–
BASIC GRAY	109120*	109121*	–	–	–	108692	108691	–	–	–
BASIC BLACK	101179*	102512*	100082	102192	102995	102851	106532	–	104581*	104582*
assorted			(set of 4)** $10.95			36 sheets (6 ea. of 6 colors)*** $7.95	24 sheets (4 ea. of 6 colors)*** $8.95	24 sheets (4 ea. of 6 colors)*** $11.95		
NEUTRALS	–	–	109126			108588	108589	108693	–	–

Idea Book & Catalog

The Idea Book & Catalog offers more than 200 pages of Stampin' Up! stamp sets, accessories, and product ideas—all at your fingertips. With hundreds of full-color samples, the Idea Book & Catalog is packed with inspiration you can use again and again!

117733   2009-2010 Idea Book & Catalog $9.95

Color Coach

Our double-sided Color Coach features coordinating and complementary color suggestions for our exclusive colors, plus a convenient chart of neutral and monochromatic color choices.

105796   Color Coach® $9.95

Card Stock

Stampin' Up!'s exclusive 80 lb, high-quality card stock is dyed with pure color all the way through. Available as color family assortments and as individual color packages. Our card stock is acid free, lignin free, and buffered, qualities that make them safe for use in scrapbooks.

Ink Pads

Our ink pads feature a flip-top design that stores the inking surface upside-down, so it stays moist between re-inkings. Use our Classic Stampin' Pads when you need fast-drying, dye-based inks. Our Craft Stampin' Pads contain rich pigment inks that are ideal for scrapbooking, embossing, and other craft projects. Index labels are available online.

sm While most of Stampin' Up!'s products are safe for your scrapbooks, our Stampin' Memories symbol identifies those that were specifically created for and are the best choice for scrapbooking.

*BASIC BROWN, BASIC BLACK, AND BASIC GRAY CLASSIC INKS ARE WATERPROOF.
**BASIC BLACK, SAHARA SAND, GOING GRAY, BASIC GRAY
***WHISPER WHITE, VERY VANILLA, SAHARA SAND, GOING GRAY, BASIC BLACK, BASIC GRAY

bold brights

	Classic		markers	Craft		card stock			cartridges	
	stampin' pad $5.95	ink refill $2.95	stampin' write $3.25	stampin' pad $7.50	ink refill $4.25	8-1/2" x 11" (24 sheets) $5.50	12" x 12" (20 sheets) $7.50	12" x 12" textured	standard cartridge $5.25	jumbo cartridge $7.50
GLORIOUS GREEN	103040	101453	100047	101436	100434	101697	106539	–	102212	103676
GREEN GALORE	102122	101735	100048	101325	102772	101768	107110	–	–	–
GABLE GREEN	101673	101483	100049	101671	101232	102795	107109	–	–	–
YOYO YELLOW	102717	101986	100050	101608	103325	102824	107108	–	–	–
ONLY ORANGE	102696	102931	100051	101951	102111	102837	107107	–	–	–
REAL RED	103133	103287	100052	101190	102104	102482	106545	–	102996	103675
PINK PASSION	101212	102308	100053	102916	103036	102762	107106	–	–	–
PIXIE PINK	105212	105224	105112	105236	105150	105121	107105	–	105203	–
ORCHID OPULENCE	101859	101324	100055	101900	100464	100969	107104	–	–	–
LOVELY LILAC	102874	103077	100056	102965	101695	100427	106541	–	–	103677
BRILLIANT BLUE	100691	100763	100057	101843	103006	100721	106540	–	100871	103674
TEMPTING TURQUOISE	100814	101041	100058	100741	100957	102067	107103	–	101199	–

assorted									stampin' spots	
	(set of 12) $57.95	(set of 12) $28.95	(set of 12) $31.95	(set of 12) $80.95	(set of 12) $45.95	36 sheets (3 ea. of 12 colors) $7.95	24 sheets (2 ea. of 12 colors) $8.95	24 sheets (2 ea. of 12 colors) $11.95	Classic (set of 12) $22.50	Craft (set of 12) $25.95
BOLD BRIGHTS	105562	105554	105538	105558	105443	105548	106528	108698	105550	105439

earth elements

	Classic		markers	Craft		card stock			cartridges	
	stampin' pad $5.95	ink refill $2.95	stampin' write $3.25	stampin' pad $7.50	ink refill $4.25	8-1/2" x 11" (24 sheets) $5.50	12" x 12" (20 sheets) $7.50	12" x 12" textured	standard cartridge $5.25	jumbo cartridge $7.50
CHOCOLATE CHIP	100908	101065	100071	101816	102847	102128	107102	–	102496	–
CLOSE TO COCOA	103139	102444	100072	100549	100925	101341	107101	–	100714	–
CREAMY CARAMEL	103220	101478	100078	103034	102004	102514	106536	–	–	–
MORE MUSTARD	103162	101962	100076	103092	101990	100946	106542	–	–	103672
PUMPKIN PIE	105216	105229	105115	105240	105164	105117	107100	–	105200	–
REALLY RUST	102549	100685	100073	102437	103014	100661	107099	–	–	–
RUBY RED	102259	100532	100075	101009	102448	102030	106537	–	–	103673
CAMEO CORAL	103035	102238	100074	101933	101033	100475	107098	–	–	–
SUMMER SUN	100537	101231	100077	101690	102765	103124	107097	–	–	–
OLD OLIVE	102277	100531	100079	103063	101425	100702	106544	–	–	103670
GARDEN GREEN	102272	102059	100080	101841	100519	102584	107096	–	–	–
NOT QUITE NAVY	103008	102949	100059	103227	102310	101722	107095	–	–	–

assorted									stampin' spots	
	(set of 12) $57.95	(set of 12) $28.95	(set of 12) $31.95	(set of 12) $80.95	(set of 12) $45.95	36 sheets (3 ea. of 12 colors) $7.95	24 sheets (2 ea. of 12 colors) $8.95	24 sheets (2 ea. of 12 colors) $11.95	Classic (set of 12) $22.50	Craft (set of 12) $25.95
EARTH ELEMENTS	105563	105555	105539	105559	105442	105566	106527	108697	105551	105438

rich regals

	Classic		markers	Craft		card stock			cartridges	
	stampin' pad $5.95	ink refill $2.95	stampin' write $3.25	stampin' pad $7.50	ink refill $4.25	8-1/2" x 11" (24 sheets) $5.50	12" x 12" (20 sheets) $7.50	12" x 12" textured	standard cartridge $5.25	jumbo cartridge $7.50
BORDERING BLUE	102265	100940	100070	101374	102530	102630	107092	–	–	–
BROCADE BLUE	101102	100408	100064	101593	100788	101166	107091	–	–	–
BALLET BLUE	100907	101713	100066	102855	101732	100613	106538	–	102305	103662
NIGHT OF NAVY	102977	103033	100069	103181	103131	100867	106547	–	–	103664
TAKEN WITH TEAL	103257	100550	100068	100617	102049	101584	107090	–	–	–
HANDSOME HUNTER	105215	105227	105116	105239	105163	105122	106534	–	105198	105205
ALWAYS ARTICHOKE	105219	105232	105113	105243	105177	105119	107089	–	105199	–
SO SAFFRON	105213	105225	105114	105237	105151	105118	107088	–	105201	–
REGAL ROSE	105211	105223	105108	105235	105149	105130	107087	–	–	–
ROSE RED	101778	102109	100063	101545	102915	102544	107086	–	–	–
BRAVO BURGUNDY	105214	105226	105109	105238	105162	105123	106533	–	105197	105207
ELEGANT EGGPLANT	105210	105222	105110	105234	105148	105126	107085	–	–	–
assorted	(set of 12) $57.95	(set of 12) $28.95	(set of 12) $31.95	(set of 12) $80.95	(set of 12) $45.95	36 sheets (3 ea. of 12 colors) $7.95	24 sheets (2 ea. of 12 colors) $8.95	24 sheets (2 ea. of 12 colors) $11.95	stampin' spots Classic (set of 12) $22.50	stampin' spots Craft (set of 12) $25.95
RICH REGALS	105564	105556	105540	105560	105440	105567	106526	108696	105552	105437

soft subtles

	Classic		markers	Craft		card stock			cartridges	
	stampin' pad $5.95	ink refill $2.95	stampin' write $3.25	stampin' pad $7.50	ink refill $4.25	8-1/2" x 11" (24 sheets) $5.50	12" x 12" (20 sheets) $7.50	12" x 12" textured	standard cartridge $5.25	jumbo cartridge $7.50
PERFECT PLUM	101437	102107	100035	102869	100697	101889	107084	–	–	103666
PALE PLUM	102732	101268	100036	103271	102202	101658	107083	–	–	–
PRETTY IN PINK	101301	102295	100045	100857	101127	100459	106546	–	–	103668
BLUSH BLOSSOM	102609	100614	100037	102080	100935	103318	107082	–	–	–
APRICOT APPEAL	105218	105231	105107	105242	105166	105124	107081	–	–	–
BARELY BANANA	101170	100639	100039	101609	101676	102701	106543	–	–	–
CERTAINLY CELERY	105217	105230	105106	105241	105165	105125	107080	–	105194	–
MELLOW MOSS	102774	101771	100038	101054	101967	102898	106548	–	–	103667
SAGE SHADOW	102532	100720	100040	103251	100711	101563	107079	–	–	–
BASHFUL BLUE	105209	105221	105111	105233	105146	105120	106535	–	105204	105206
ALMOST AMETHYST	101723	102580	100043	101211	102282	102158	107078	–	–	–
LAVENDER LACE	101305	100862	100041	103144	101590	101614	107077	–	101812	–
assorted	(set of 12) $57.95	(set of 12) $28.95	(set of 12) $31.95	(set of 12) $80.95	(set of 12) $45.95	36 sheets (3 ea. of 12 colors) $7.95	24 sheets (2 ea. of 12 colors) $8.95	24 sheets (2 ea. of 12 colors) $11.95	stampin' spots Classic (set of 12) $22.50	stampin' spots Craft (set of 12) $25.95
SOFT SUBTLES	105565	105557	105537	105561	105441	105568	106525	108695	105553	105370

When you're selecting a color scheme, our neutral palette provides the perfect complement to any color combination. Choose the color you like best, or try our specialty paper to achieve a textured look.

distinctive accents

BRIDE   GROOM   BRIDESMAID

♡ Specialty Paper

Use this elegant, foiled Whisper White, Basic Black and Very Vanilla card stock to create wedding invitations, RSVP cards, place settings, party favors, and more! The foil gives the paper shine, pattern, and texture. Includes 5 sheets ea. in 2 designs: pin stripe and damask. 12" x 12". (Whisper White, Vanilla/Pearl foil and Basic Black/Black foil)

☐	115669	Bride Whisper White	$13.95
■	116478	Groom Basic Black	$13.95
☐	116479	Bridesmaid Very Vanilla	$13.95

Sticky Pages

Use sheets to cover On Board albums with Designer Series paper or create your own Sticky Cuts with the Big Shot. These are only two of the possibilities with these sticky sheets! See what you can create. Pkg. of 2. 12" x 12".

114300	Sticky Pages	$6.95

Wood Sheets

Create unique and textured die cuts with our Wood Sheets, sized for use with the Big Shot. Includes four 5-3/4" x 13-3/4" sheets.

116309	Texture Cuts	$9.95

Window Sheets

How do you use window sheets? Let us count the ways. Use them on scrapbook pages, embellish them with Rub-Ons that you then use as overlays, or layer them on card stock. Create shapes and clear packages or windows in cards and boxes with the Big Shot die-cut machine. Sponge the edges with Craft ink to add color. There are countless options! Includes two (2) 12" x 12" sheets.

114323	Window Sheets Medium	$4.95
114324	Window Sheets Thick	$6.95

Décor Elements Sheets

Create your own Décor Elements using these sheets and our Sizzix dies. Each package comes with two (2) 12" x 24" sheets of vinyl in specified color, along with two (2) 12" x 24" sheets of transfer tape to make using your vinyl pieces easy to use. Instructions for use are included in the package.

■	114336	Kraft	$12.95
■	114337	Chocolate	$12.95
☐	114335	White	$12.95
■	114334	Dark Gray	$12.95

Watercolor Paper

100%-cotton, cold-pressed 140 lb. watercolor paper. Sized perfectly to layer on your card front. 3-3/4" x 5".

105019	Watercolor Paper (20)	$6.95

PAPER PATTERN SWATCHES SHOWN AT 50%

naturals

WHISPER WHITE	VERY VANILLA	KRAFT	NATURALS WHITE
CONFETTI WHITE	SHIMMERY WHITE	NATURALS IVORY	CONFETTI CREAM
GLOSSY WHITE	BRUSHED GOLD	BRUSHED SILVER	WHITE VELLUM

Card Stock 12" x 12" *sm*

106529	Whisper White (20) *a,l,b*	$7.50
106530	Very Vanilla (20) *a,l,b*	$7.50
107070	Kraft (20) *a,l,b*	$7.50

Card Stock 8-1/2" x 11"

100730	Whisper White (40) *a,l,b*	*sm*	$7.50
101650	Very Vanilla (40) *a,l,b*	*sm*	$7.50
102125	Kraft (40) *a,l,b*	*sm*	$7.50
102316	Naturals White (40) *a,l,b*	*sm*	$7.50
102028	Confetti White (40) *a,l,b*	*sm*	$9.50
101910	Shimmery White (10)		$7.95
101849	Naturals Ivory (40) *a,l,b*	*sm*	$7.50
102835	Confetti Cream (40) *a,l,b*	*sm*	$9.50
102599	Glossy White (25)		$5.95
102935	Brushed Gold (10) *a*		$7.95
100712	Brushed Silver (10) *a*		$7.95

White Vellum *sm*

101856	8-1/2" x 11" Card Stock (20) *a,l*	$6.50
101839	8-1/2" x 11" Paper (20) *a,l*	$4.95

bags & calendars

Cellophane Bags
50 per pkg.

103104	Small Flat (3" x 5")	$3.95
102757	Medium Flat (4" x 6")	$4.50
102210	Large Flat (6" x 8")	$4.95

Birthday Calendar
Keep track of birthdays and other important occasions with these perpetual date trackers. Acid free, lignin free, and buffered. 5-1/2" x 14". *sm*

101398	Whisper White	$7.95

Days-To-Remember Calendar
Scrapbook pages you create enliven each month. The perforated pages can be removed from the calendar and added to an album. Acid free, lignin free, and buffered. Whisper White. *sm*

104144	6" x 6" Desktop Calendar	$9.95

Treat Boxes
Use our coated, food-safe treat boxes for gifts and all kinds of treats. Boxes ship flat, ready to assemble. Approx. dimensions: 4-5/8" x 2-3/8" x 6-1/8". 5 per package.

	115690	Treat Boxes	$3.95
		Chocolate Chip, Close to Cocoa	

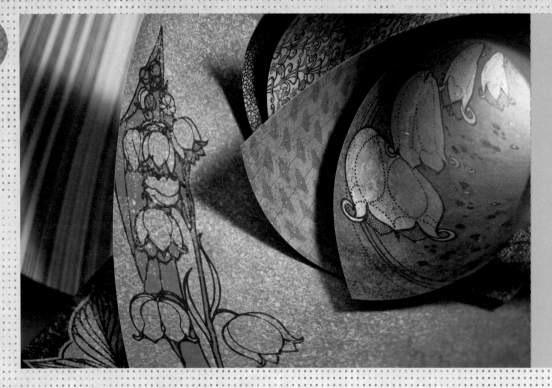

Our 12" x 12" Designer Series paper features exclusive patterns printed on both sides. The coordinating card stock colors are listed below each paper assortment. All sheets can be trimmed to create 6" x 6" and 8-1/2" x 11" pages. 12 sheets: 2 ea. of 6 double-sided designs. Acid and lignin free. *sm*

designer series paper

115670 Nouveau Chic Basic Black, Basic Gray, Sage Shadow, Apricot Appeal		$9.95
115672 Merry Moments Chocolate Chip, Real Red, Old Olive, Garden Green, Very Vanilla		$9.95
115671 Cottage Wall Old Olive, Orchid Opulence, Rich Razzleberry		$9.95
115668 Autumn Traditions Elegant Eggplant, Soft Suede, Ruby Red, More Mustard, Always Artichoke		$9.95

115677   Cast-A-Spell   **$9.95**
Basic Black, Old Olive, Pumpkin Pie, Perfect Plum

115678   Tall Tales   **$9.95**
Chocolate Chip, So Saffron, Old Olive, Brilliant Blue, Rose Red

113976   Pink Flamingo   **$9.95**
Chocolate Chip, Real Red, Summer Sun, Cameo Coral, Tempting Turquoise

115680   Kaleidoscope   **$9.95**
Tempting Turquoise, Green Galore, Summer Sun,
Only Orange, Pink Passion, Pixie Pink

SHOWN IN SOFT SUEDE

Patterns Designer Series Paper

Available in 14 of our most popular colors, this paper offers a design for every project. 12 sheets: 2 ea. of 6 double-sided designs. *sm*

115684	Bermuda Bay	**$9.95**
115686	Crushed Curry	**$9.95**
115689	Dusty Durango	**$9.95**
115687	Melon Mambo	**$9.95**
115685	Rich Razzleberry	**$9.95**
115688	Soft Suede	**$9.95**
112152	So Saffron	**$9.95**
112160	Old Olive	**$9.95**
112154	Certainly Celery	**$9.95**
112151	Bashful Blue	**$9.95**
112159	Pumpkin Pie	**$9.95**
112162	Rose Red	**$9.95**
112158	Perfect Plum	**$9.95**
112164	Chocolate Chip	**$9.95**

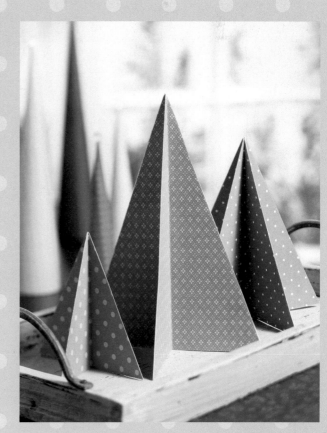

115675　Razzleberry Lemonade　$9.95
Rich Razzleberry, Crushed Curry, Melon Mambo, Pumpkin Pie

113992　Tea Party　$9.95
Certainly Celery, Pretty in Pink, Basic Gray, Almost Amethyst, So Saffron

115676　Holiday Lounge　$9.95
Taken with Teal, Ruby Red, Sahara Sand, Basic Gray

114018　Flock Together　$9.95
Tempting Turquoise, Certainly Celery, So Saffron, Garden Green

113974　Bella Bleu　$9.95
Very Vanilla, Kraft, Not Quite Navy

113995　Jackpot　$9.95
Basic Black, Real Red, So Saffron, Very Vanilla

Use our Specialty Designer Series paper for all your crafting and home décor projects. Our selection of patterns and colors makes it wonderfully versatile. Some assortments are printed on textured paper and some include die-cut pieces.

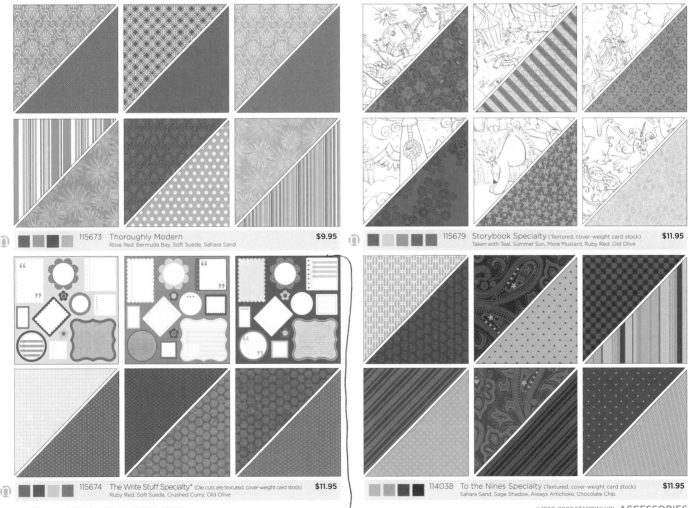

115673 Thoroughly Modern $9.95
Rose Red, Bermuda Bay, Soft Suede, Sahara Sand

115679 Storybook Specialty (Textured, cover-weight card stock) $11.95
Taken with Teal, Summer Sun, More Mustard, Ruby Red, Old Olive

115674 The Write Stuff Specialty* (Die cuts are textured, cover-weight card stock) $11.95
Ruby Red, Soft Suede, Crushed Curry, Old Olive

114038 To the Nines Specialty (Textured, cover-weight card stock) $11.95
Sahara Sand, Sage Shadow, Always Artichoke, Chocolate Chip

ALL PAPER PATTERN SWATCHES SHOWN AT 25%
*2 EA. OF 3 DOUBLE-SIDED DESIGNS (6), 1 EA. OF 3 DIE-CUT SHEETS, SINGLE-SIDED TEXTURED COVER-WEIGHT (3).

Preserve your photos with our coordinated Simply Scrappin' kits, complete with self-adhesive die cuts, patterned paper, and card stock. Trim sheets with the Paper Cutter (page 191) to create 6" x 6" and 8-1/2" x 11" pages. *sm*

simply scrappin'

115700   Sunny Day $19.95

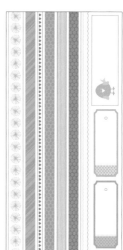

3 SHEETS EA. 12" x 12" DOUBLE-SIDED PAPER

| PINK PASSION | TEMPTING TURQUOISE | PUMPKIN PIE | OLD OLIVE |

2 SHEETS EA. 12" x 12" TEXTURED CARD STOCK

2 SHEETS EA. 6" x 12" SELF-ADHESIVE DIE CUTS

The coordinating Cheep Talk and Good Friend sets are shown on pages 112-113, and samples are shown above. The coordinating On Board So Tweet is shown on page 185.

ALL PAPER PATTERN SWATCHES SHOWN AT 25%

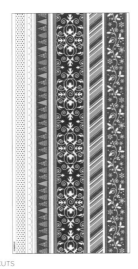

2 SHEETS EA. 6" x 12" SELF-ADHESIVE DIE CUTS

115696   Christmas Jingle   **$19.95**

3 SHEETS EA. 12" x 12" DOUBLE-SIDED PAPER

| CHOCOLATE CHIP | REAL RED | OLD OLIVE | VERY VANILLA |

2 SHEETS EA. 12" x 12" TEXTURED CARD STOCK

The coordinating Tree Trimmings set and sample made from this kit are shown on page 28.

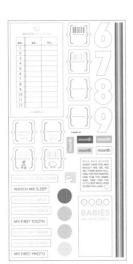

2 SHEETS EA. 6" x 12" SELF-ADHESIVE DIE CUTS

115694   Moments & Milestones   **$19.95**

3 SHEETS EA. 12" x 12" DOUBLE-SIDED PAPER

| CERTAINLY CELERY | TEMPTING TURQUOISE | SO SAFFRON | BASIC GRAY |

2 SHEETS EA. 12" x 12" TEXTURED CARD STOCK

The coordinating Cute & Cuddly set is shown on page 77.

2 SHEETS EA. 6" x 12" SELF-ADHESIVE DIE CUTS

115699   Cool Kids   **$19.95**

3 SHEETS EA. 12" x 12" DOUBLE-SIDED PAPER
(PAPER IS DESIGNED TO BE CUT DOWN FOR 6" x 6" ALBUMS)

| BASHFUL BLUE | REAL RED | CRUSHED CURRY | BASIC GRAY |

2 SHEETS EA. 12" x 12" TEXTURED CARD STOCK

The coordinating Lots of Bots set is shown on page 82.

115695 Happy B-day   **$19.95**

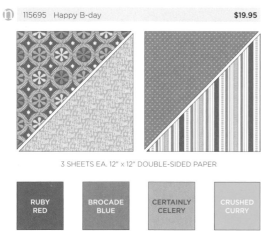

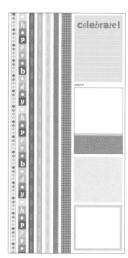

3 SHEETS EA. 12" x 12" DOUBLE-SIDED PAPER

| RUBY RED | BROCADE BLUE | CERTAINLY CELERY | CRUSHED CURRY |

2 SHEETS EA. 12" x 12" TEXTURED CARD STOCK

2 SHEETS EA. 6" x 12" SELF-ADHESIVE DIE CUTS

115697 Guest Book   **$19.95**

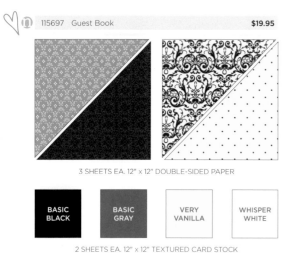

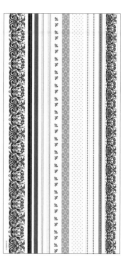

3 SHEETS EA. 12" x 12" DOUBLE-SIDED PAPER

| BASIC BLACK | BASIC GRAY | VERY VANILLA | WHISPER WHITE |

2 SHEETS EA. 12" x 12" TEXTURED CARD STOCK

The coordinating Monogram Sweet set is shown on pages 49 and 151.

2 SHEETS EA. 6" x 12" SELF-ADHESIVE DIE CUTS

113059 Petal Party   **$19.95**

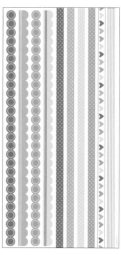

3 SHEETS EA. 12" x 12" DOUBLE-SIDED PAPER

| OLD OLIVE | SO SAFFRON | PUMPKIN PIE | PIXIE PINK |

2 SHEETS EA. 12" x 12" TEXTURED CARD STOCK

The coordinating Best Wishes & More set is shown on page 64.

2 SHEETS EA. 6" x 12" SELF-ADHESIVE DIE CUTS

ALL PAPER PATTERN SWATCHES SHOWN AT 25%

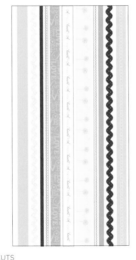

2 SHEETS EA. 6" x 12" SELF-ADHESIVE DIE CUTS

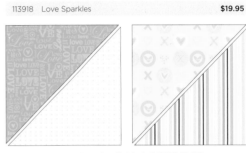

113918   Love Sparkles $19.95

3 SHEETS EA. 12" x 12" DOUBLE-SIDED PAPER

| CHOCOLATE CHIP | REGAL ROSE | WHISPER WHITE | SO SAFFRON |

2 SHEETS EA. 12" x 12" TEXTURED CARD STOCK

The coordinating A Happy Heart set is shown on page 45.

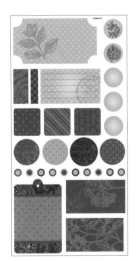

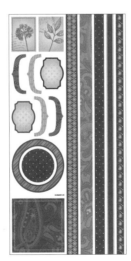

2 SHEETS EA. 6" x 12" SELF-ADHESIVE DIE CUTS

114326   Tailor Made $19.95

3 SHEETS EA. 12" x 12" DOUBLE-SIDED PAPER

| NOT QUITE NAVY | ALWAYS ARTICHOKE | CHOCOLATE CHIP | SAHARA SAND |

2 SHEETS EA. 12" x 12" TEXTURED CARD STOCK

The coordinating Le Jardin Botanique set is shown on page 110.

Nothing says "I'm thinking of you" like a unique, handcrafted card. Stampin' Up! offers products to help you create endless styles and sizes. Tuck your creation into one of our signature envelopes that feature our exclusive, rounded flap.

cards and envelopes

MEDIUM: 5-3/4" x 4-3/8"

Medium Envelopes

107301	Whisper White (40)	**$6.50**
107300	Very Vanilla (40)	**$6.50**
107297	Kraft (40)	**$6.50**
107302	Natural Ivory (40)	**$6.50**
107303	Natural White (40)	**$6.50**
102619	Clear Translucent (50)	**$4.95**
	(May require extra postage; square flap)	

Medium Square Envelopes

107289	Medium Whisper White (20)	**$6.50**
	(May require extra postage)	

Mini Square Envelopes

107309	Whisper White (40)	**$7.50**
	(U.S. Postal Service will not process or deliver)	

MEDIUM: 5-1/2" x 5-1/2"
MINI: 3-1/8" x 3-1/8"

Small Open-End Envelopes

107286	Whisper White (20)	**$7.50**

SMALL: 6-3/4" x 3-1/2"

CARD: 5" x 3-1/2"
ENVELOPE: 5-1/8" x 3-5/8"

Note Cards

Classic note cards include 20 ea. Whisper White cards and envelopes.

107311	Note Cards Whisper White	**$5.95**

CARD: 4" x 4"
ENVELOPE: 4-1/4" x 4-1/4"

Elegant Notes

Use our Elegant Notes to create cards both graceful and timeless. Includes 15 Very Vanilla cards and envelopes.

116450	Elegant Notes Very Vanilla (U.S. Postal Service will not process or deliver)	**$9.95**

CARD: 4" x 4"
ENVELOPE: 4-1/4" x 4-1/4"

Pendant Notes

Our die-cut Pendant Notes feature a detailed, formal design and coordinate with the Pendant Park set (page 118). Includes 15 Kraft cards and envelopes.

116449	Pendant Notes Kraft (U.S. Postal Service will not process or deliver)	**$8.95**

CARD: 4" x 4"
ENVELOPE: 4-1/4" x 4-1/4"

Fresh-Cut Notes

Fresh-Cut Notes coordinate with the Fresh Cuts set (page 107) and the 5-Petal Flower punch (page 186). Includes 15 ea. Whisper White cards and envelopes.

111882	Fresh-Cut Notes Whisper White (U.S. Postal Service will not process or deliver)	**$8.95**

die cuts

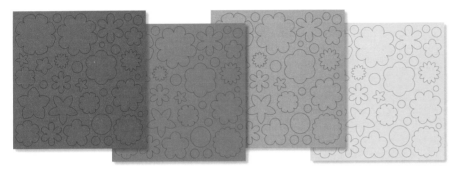

Die Cuts

Make multicolor die-cut blossoms with our Blooms. Mix and match the pieces until you've got them just right. Four 12" x 12" sheets: 1 of ea. color.

	111376	Blooms Real Red, Old Olive, Pumpkin Pie, Bashful Blue	$8.95

designer printed

FLOWER FANTASY*   SEASONAL PIECES   CLEARLY THANKS

Printed Window Sheets

Our printed window sheets offer beautiful designs in a variety of shapes great for overlays and photo frames. 2 sheets each.

	115705	Flower Fantasy* (12" x 12") Rich Razzleberry, Old Olive, White, Orchid Opulence	$7.95
	115706	Seasonal Pieces (12" x 12") White, Vanilla, Chocolate Chip	$7.95
	115122	Clearly Thanks (8-1/2" x 11") White	$5.95

SAHARA SAND REPRESENTS THE TRANSPARENT PORTION. *COORDINATES WITH THE COTTAGE WALL DESIGNER SERIES PAPER (PAGE 160).

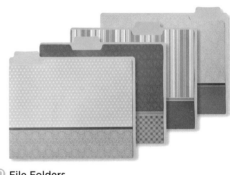

File Folders

Coordinates with the Thoroughly Modern Designer Series paper (page 163) and Modern Label punch (page 186). Includes 12 folders: 3 ea. of 4 designs. Approx. dimensions: 11-3/4" x 8-7/8".

	115692	Thoroughly Modern Rose Red, Sahara Sand, Soft Suede, Bermuda Bay	$10.95

Gusseted Envelopes

Coordinates with the Thoroughly Modern Designer Series paper (page 163). Includes 3 envelopes: 1 ea. of 3 designs. Approx. dimensions: 10" x 5-1/4".

	115693	Thoroughly Modern Rose Red, Sahara Sand, Soft Suede, Bermuda Bay	$5.95

Enjoy the ease of having a stamp set and coordinating accessories chosen for you. With our kits, you'll take the guesswork out of card making—and create cards you can use all year long.

simply sent® card kits

Birthday Wishes

From the Heart

kit contents
4-Piece Die-cut Stamp Set
Elegant Eggplant Classic Stampin' Spot
Old Olive Classic Stampin' Spot
Chocolate Chip Classic Stampin' Spot
Card Stock Assortment
Aqua Painter
5/8" Very Vanilla Grosgrain Ribbon
1/4" Old Olive Grosgrain Ribbon
Stampin' Dimensionals
Mini Glue Dots
Very Vanilla 4-1/4" x 4-1/4" Square Envelopes

KIT CREATES 10 CARDS (5 EA. IN 2 STYLES)
CARD SIZE: 4" x 4"*

Simply Sent Card Kit
Use our Simply Sent Card Kits to create gorgeous cards in minutes. Then use the stamp set to create dozens of other projects! You'll love the versatile images offered in this kit. Project instructions are included.

 115704   Petite Pansies   **$42.95**
Elegant Eggplant, Perfect Plum, Old Olive, Close to Cocoa, Very Vanilla

*U.S. POSTAL SERVICE WILL NOT PROCESS OR DELIVER.

kit contents

5-Piece Die-cut Stamp Set
Not Quite Navy Classic Stampin' Spot
Really Rust Classic Stampin' Spot
Card Stock Assortment
3/4" Round Clear Buttons
Pewter Mini Library Clips
On Board Pieces
3/8" Kraft Taffeta Ribbon
1/4" Sage Shadow Grosgrain Ribbon
Linen Thread
Stampin' Dimensionals
Mini Glue Dots
Whisper White 4-1/4" x 4-1/4" Square Envelopes

KIT CREATES 10 CARDS (5 EA. IN 2 STYLES)
CARD SIZE: 4" x 4"*

Simply Sent Card Kit

Use our Simply Sent Card Kits to create gorgeous cards in minutes. Then use the stamp set to create dozens of other projects! You'll love the versatile images offered in this kit. Project instructions are included.

115703   For You Phrases $42.95
Kraft, Sage Shadow, Really Rust, Not Quite Navy

---

kit contents

5-Piece Die-cut Stamp Set
VersaMark Cube
Bashful Blue Classic Stampin' Spot
Chocolate Chip Classic Stampin' Spot
Card Stock and Textured Card Stock Assortments
Designer Series Paper Assortment
1/4" Chocolate Chip Grosgrain Ribbon
3/8" Kraft Taffeta Ribbon
Pewter Vintage Brads
3/8" Bashful Blue Round Buttons
Stampin' Dimensionals
Mini Glue Dots
Kraft 6-3/4" x 3-1/2" Open-End Envelopes

KIT CREATES 10 CARDS (5 EA. IN 2 STYLES)
CARD SIZE: 3" x 6"

Simply Sent Card Kit

Use our Simply Sent Card Kits to create gorgeous cards in minutes. Then use the stamp set to create dozens of other projects! You'll love the versatile images offered in this kit. Project instructions are included.

114598   No One Like You $42.95
Bashful Blue, Kraft, Chocolate Chip, Very Vanilla

HAPPY
birthday

thanks

Simply Sent Card Elements & More

Our Simply Sent Card Elements & More include the products you need to create unforgettable projects. Your cards will come together quickly—and you'll have a stamp set you can use for other projects. Product instructions are included.

114579   2U   **$24.95**
Chocolate Chip, Very Vanilla, Tempting Turquoise (May require extra postage)

thank you

thanks

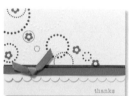

Simply Sent Card Elements & More

Our Simply Sent Card Elements & More include the products you need to create unforgettable projects. Your cards will come together quickly—and you'll have a stamp set you can use for other projects. Product instructions are included.

114594   Thanks x 2   **$24.95**
Chocolate Chip, Old Olive, Whisper White

SO VERY **HAPPY** FOR **YOU**!

YOU ARE **IN** MY **THOUGHTS**

Simply Sent Card Elements & More

Our Simply Sent Card Elements & More include the products you need to create unforgettable projects. Your cards will come together quickly—and you'll have a stamp set you can use for other projects. Product instructions are included.

114585   It's About You   **$24.95**
Bashful Blue, Pumpkin Pie, So Saffron, Garden Green (May require extra postage)

simply sent card elements

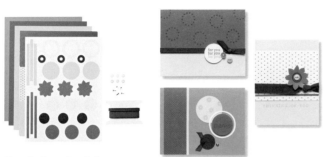

Simply Sent Card Elements

Kit includes 2 sheets each of 8-1/2" x 11" Bashful Blue, Ruby Red, and Kraft card stock; 1 sheet 8-1/2" x 11" self-adhesive die cuts; 2 sheets 8-1/2" x 11" single-sided Designer Series paper; Chocolate Chip 5/8" grosgrain ribbon, Chocolate Chip 1/4" grosgrain ribbon, Styled Silver brads, Bashful Blue buttons, Very Vanilla buttons (stamp set, adhesive, and ink not included).

114572	Thankful Thinking	$15.95
	Ruby Red, Bashful Blue, Chocolate Chip, Very Vanilla, Kraft	

Thankful Thinking
113786 **$13.95** | SET OF 6

Pensamientos de agradecimiento
114020 **ESP**

Simply Sent Card Elements

Kit includes 2 sheets each of 8-1/2" x 11" Rose Red, Old Olive and Perfect Plum textured card stock; 1 sheet 8-1/2" x 11" Self-adhesive die cuts; 2 sheets each of 8-1/2" x 11" double-sided Designer Series paper; Whisper White 1/4" grosgrain ribbon; More Mustard 1/4" grosgrain ribbon; More Mustard buttons; Old Olive buttons; More Mustard brads (stamp set, adhesive, and ink not included).

112028	Flower Power	$15.95
	Rose Red, Old Olive, Perfect Plum, More Mustard	

Wow Flowers
111714 **$12.95** | SET OF 4

Flores llamativas **ESP** | Bonheur fleuri **FRA**
112955 | 112652

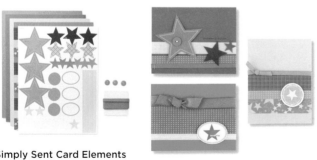

Simply Sent Card Elements

Kit includes 2 sheets each of 8-1/2" x 11" Bashful Blue, Old Olive, and More Mustard textured card stock; 1 sheet 8-1/2" x 11" self-adhesive die cuts; 2 sheets each of 8-1/2" x 11" double-sided Designer Series paper; Old Olive 5/8" grosgrain ribbon; More Mustard 1/4" grosgrain ribbon; More Mustard buttons (stamp set, adhesive, and ink not included).

112021	Rock Star	$15.95
	Bashful Blue, Old Olive, More Mustard, Brilliant Blue	

ESP Elementos para tarjetas estrella de rock Simply Sent
112962

Starring You
111696 **$13.95** | SET OF 4

Celebremos **ESP**
112949

Our Party Kits make it easy to find the party. The cute decorations, pennants, and food toppers are sure to say the party is right here. Available in two styles, our Party Kits include dozens of pieces to make your party fun, easy, and fantastic.

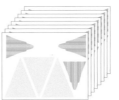

8 ENVELOPES

8 SHEETS
CROWN DECORATIONS

2 SHEETS
INVITATIONS, FOOD TOPPERS

4 SHEETS
PENNANTS

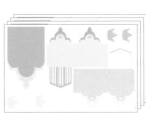

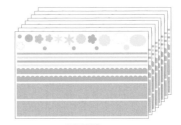

4 SHEETS
PENNANTS, PURSE BOXES, FOOD TOPPERS

8 SHEETS
CROWNS, DECORATIONS

Princess Party Kit

These die-cut pieces make it easy to create party items with a princess theme. Kit creates 8 invitations and envelopes, 8 purse boxes, 8 crowns, 24 food toppers with picks, and 20 paper pennants. Kit also includes White 1/4" grosgrain ribbon (17 yds). Coordinates with the Princess Personalized Name Stamp (page 75). Assembly required, adhesive not included.

116214   Princess Party   **$15.95**
Regal Rose, Pretty in Pink, Barely Banana, Bashful Blue, Pale Plum, Certainly Celery

Princess Time
116720   **$16.95**

SET OF 6

1 SHEET
SELF-ADHESIVE PRINTED EYE PATCHES

1 SHEET
CHIPBOARD EYE PATCHES

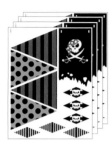

8 ENVELOPES

4 SHEETS
PENNANTS, FOOD TOPPERS

2 SHEETS
INVITATIONS

4 SHEETS
TREASURE CHEST BOXES

 Pirate Time 116718 **$16.95** SET OF 5

 Pirate Party Kit

These die-cut pieces make it easy to create party items with a pirate theme. Kit creates 8 invitations and envelopes, 8 treasure-chest boxes, 8 chipboard eye patches, 24 food toppers with picks, and 20 paper pennants. Kit also includes Black 1/4" grosgrain ribbon (6 yds) and Black elastic cord (7 yds). Coordinates with the Pirate Personalized Name Stamp (page 74). Assembly required; adhesive not included.

♡ 116213 **Pirate Party** $15.95
Real Red, Chocolate Chip, Basic Black, More Mustard,
So Saffron, Taken with Teal, Garden Green

Turn to pages 74–75 for a closer look at all the treasures you'll find in the Pirate Party Kit!

holiday photo card kit

 Holiday Photo Card Kit

Create your own holiday cards. Designed to be used with 4" x 6" photos, kit includes 12 printed cards, 6 sheets 7-3/4" x 9-1/2" self-adhesive die cuts, and 12 Very Vanilla envelopes. Stamp set and ink not included. Finished card size: 5" x 7"

115667 **Holiday Photo Card Kit** **$19.95**
Real, Red, Old Olive,
Close to Cocoa, Kraft, Very Vanilla

May the joy and love
you feel this holiday season
extend to every day
throughout the year.

Merry Christmas

Christmas Greetings 115448 **$10.95** SET OF 2

Chew, chew, I like you!

Thank you so much

Our Rub-Ons are easy to apply and enhance any card stock, patterned paper, or stamped image. The eye-catching images are designed to complement many of our stamp sets, so your creations will be easy to coordinate. 5-7/8" x 12", 2 sheets in every package.

rub-ons

115728   Dots & Designs   **$11.95**
Chocolate Chip, Ruby Red, Whisper White

115730   Dotted Delicates   **$11.95**
More Mustard, Bravo Burgundy, Always Artichoke

115725   So Cool   **$11.95**
Certainly Celery, Bashful Blue, Basic Gray, Bermuda Bay

| | 115729 | Spooky Treats | $10.95 |

Whisper White, Basic Black

| | 115731 | Autumn Harvest | $10.95 |

Whisper White, Chocolate Chip

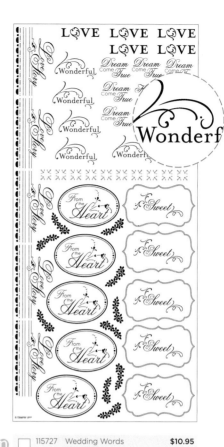

| | 115727 | Wedding Words | $10.95 |

Whisper White

| | 113886 | Planter Box | $10.95 |

Whisper White, Chocolate Chip

Thank you so much
I appreciate all you do
Thanks for being there
So grateful for you
Thanks for all you do
From my heart, thanks
Thanks for being you
THANKS A MILLION!
Thanks for everything
SO THANKFUL
FRIENDS FOREVER
You mean a lot to me
My dear, kind friend
My wonderful friend
Friend, you're the best!
HELLO FRIEND!
Just saying hello!
Thinking of you, friend
Friends make us strong
You make me laugh
Happy birthday to
a great friend!
Hope your special
day is wonderful!
Happy birthday,
my dear friend
Have a super
happy birthday!
Birthdays are awesome!
So are you!
Just for you
on your birthday!
Wishing you the best
birthday ever!
BIRTHDAYS
are the best!

Welcome, little one
tiny feet, tiny hands
SO HAPPY FOR YOU
CONGRATULATIONS
SWEET NEW BABY
for you and baby
BUNDLE OF JOY
precious little one
a new little someone
adorable little baby
GET WELL SOON
hope you feel better
think happy thoughts
THINKING OF YOU
GET WELL WISHES
heartfelt wishes
thoughts and prayers
I'M HERE FOR YOU
sending warm wishes
better get better
HAPPY HOLIDAYS
WINTER WISHES
Merry Christmas
Season's Greetings
LOVE, PEACE, JOY
DECK THE HALLS
christmas cheer
Peaceful Wishes
Merry and Bright
christmas blessings
it's time to
CELEBRATE!
Break out the
birthday cake!

LOVE ALWAYS
forever my friend
such a happy couple
bride & groom
APPLAUSE
love of a lifetime
precious little one
little baby
GET WELL SOON
XOXOXOXOXO
hugs & kisses
ALL MY LOVE
forever & always
I LOVE YOU
always on my mind
love and cherish
Easter wishes
Congrats, Grad!
Happy
Mother's Day!
Happy
FATHER'S DAY!
Be My Valentine
Happy Hanukkah
Miss you so much
A gift for you
Rock on, dude!
GOOD LUCK!
HAPPY HALLOWEEN
Welcome, Neighbor

| | 111804 | Chit Chat | $10.95 |

Whisper White, Chocolate Chip

| | 113889 | Laughter and Love | $10.95 |

Whisper White, Chocolate Chip

Eyelets, brads, Hodgepodge Hardware, and more—we've got the embellishments you need to adorn your handcrafted creations. The variety of colors and assortments available makes it easy to mix and match.

embellishments

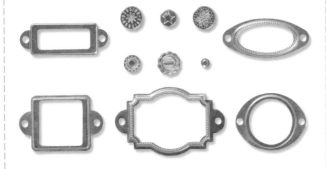

PIECES ARE SHOWN AT 50% OF ACTUAL SIZE.

kit contents

Raised Dots Designer holders (10)
Small Rectangle holders (10)
Raised Dots Designer holders (10)
1" Circle holders (10)
Square holders (10)
1/2" Genuine brads (10)
3/8" Star brads (10)
1/2" Flower Brads (10)
3/8" Flower brads (10)
Flower ribbon slides (10)
3/16" Brads (100)

SHOWN AT ACTUAL SIZE

STYLED SILVER

STYLED VANILLA

Hodgepodge Hardware

Our Hodgepodge Hardware includes fresh designs in two finishes in a reusable tin. These high quality metal accents coordinate with many of our punches.

| 111325 | Styled Silver* | $29.95 |
| 112454 | Styled Vanilla* | $29.95 |

PIECES ARE SHOWN AT 50% OF ACTUAL SIZE.

kit contents

White flowers (50: 10 ea. in 5 sizes)
White halfback pearls (30 small, 20 medium, 10 large)
Cream halfback pearls (30 small, 20 medium, 10 large)
White round pearls w/ holes (30 small, 15 large)
Cream round pearls w/ holes (30 small, 15 large)
Clear round beads w/ center hole (10)
Clear round beads w/ side hole (10)
Clear teardrops (20)
Clear round rhinestone brads
(20 small, 15 medium, 15 large)
Hat Pins w/ clutches (10)
Spacer beads (30)

Pretties Kit

Use this versatile kit to embellish all of your works of heart! Use Stampin' Pastels, Watercolor Wonder Crayons, or Classic ink to dye the flowers to coordinate with our exclusive colors. Comes in a reusable tin.

| 109114 | Pretties Kit* | $29.95 |

*CONTENT COUNTS ARE APPROXIMATE

Jumbo Brads

Our jumbo brads come in 2 sizes that are sure to suit your projects. 5/16" Neutrals assortment includes approx. 80 brads: 20 ea. of 4 colors listed below. 5/8" Neutrals assortment includes approx. 32 brads: 8 ea. of 4 colors listed below.

5/16"   5/8"

	112534	5/16" Neutrals	$7.95
		Choclate Chip, Silver, Very Vanilla, Whisper White	
	112533	5/8" Neutrals	$6.95
		Choclate Chip, Silver, Very Vanilla, Whisper White	

Build-A-Brad

Punch a 1/2" circle of Designer Series paper or stamp a custom image to build your own brad! Kit includes 24 ea. brad bases and adhesive acrylic bubbles.

109108	Antique Brass	$9.95
109128	Pewter	$9.95

Designer Brads

High-quality, cast brads come in custom Stampin' Up! designs, shapes, and finishes. Use separately or with our Hodgepodge Hardware. Unless otherwise noted, each assortment includes 16 pieces: 8 ea. of 2 sizes.

112579	Flower	$5.95
112577	Filigree (16; also includes 16 3/16" brads)	$5.95
112571	Circle	$5.95
112572	Star	$5.95
112583	Flower Assortment (32: 8 of ea. of 4 colors)	$6.95
	Pumpkin Pie, Pretty in Pink, So Saffron, Chocolate Chip	

FLOWER   CIRCLE

FILIGREE   STAR   FLOWER ASSORTMENT

Brads

Exclusive colors coordinate beautifully with many of our other accessories. Approx. 200 per container. Assortments include approx. 50 ea. of 4 colors. Shown at actual size.

	104337	Gold	$6.95
	104336	Silver	$6.95
	109109	Vintage	$8.95
		Black, Silver, Antique Brass, Pewter	
	106957	Bold Brights	$8.95
		Brilliant Blue, Green Galore, Real Red, Tempting Turquoise	
	106955	Earth Elements	$8.95
		More Mustard, Old Olive, Not Quite Navy, Ruby Red	
	106953	Rich Regals	$8.95
		Always Artichoke, Brocade Blue, Rose Red, So Saffron	
	106954	Soft Subtles	$8.95
		Apricot Appeal, Bashful Blue, Certainly Celery, Pretty in Pink	

Jumbo Eyelets

ANTIQUE BRASS   PEWTER

Work beautifully with the Crop-A-Dile. Use with On Board chipboard to make perfect rivets for altered/custom books! Approx. 60 eyelets.

108431	Antique Brass	$9.95
108432	Pewter	$9.95

Designer Hardware

Custom designed by Stampin' Up!, these painted grommets add whimsy and fun to your creations. Small assortment includes 60 pieces: 15 of ea. color. Jumbo assortment includes 20 pieces: 5 of ea. color. Use these jumbo grommets with the 1/2" Circle punch and to frame small stamped images. Use the bone folder (page 188) to set both sizes.

SMALL   JUMBO

	114349	Basic Small Grommets	$6.95
		Basic Black, Silver, Very Vanilla, Whisper White	
	114348	Basic Jumbo Grommets	$6.95
		Basic Black, Silver, Very Vanilla, Whisper White	

Clips Assortment

These exclusive clips give your projects the right touch. Assortment includes 24 pieces in our Styled Silver finish: 8 ea. 1/2" small library clip, 1/2" x 3/4" Wire clip, and 1/2" x 3/4" Wide clip.

112580	Clips Assortment	$6.95

1/2" Library Clips

Our custom-colored library clips assortment includes approx. 24 pieces: 8 ea. of 3 colors.

	112581	1/2" Library Clips	$6.95
		Chocolate Chip, Old Olive, Whisper White	

Mini Library Clips

Innovative clips offer a smaller version of your favorite library clips. Includes 12 ea. of 4 colors. Clip size: 1/4" x 1/2".

	109857	Mini Library Clips	$12.95
		Black, Silver, Antique Brass, Pewter	

Eyelets

Easily set with the Crop-A-Dile. Assortment includes approx. 50 ea. of 4 colors.

105319	Metallic	$5.95
	Gold, Silver, Copper, Antique Brass	

Rhinestone Brads

Add a bit of sparkle to any project! Each circle assortment includes approx. 80 brads: 4 colors, 3 sizes. Each square assortment includes approx. 80 brads: 4 colors, 2 sizes. Clear assortment includes approx. 84 brads: 28 ea. of 3 sizes. Small shown below.

	113144	Clear (84)	$10.95
	109110	Circle Fire	$10.95
		Pink, Red, Pumpkin, Yellow	
	109111	Circle Ice	$10.95
		Lilac, Light Blue, Turquoise, Green	
	109112	Square Fire	$10.95
		Pink, Red, Pumpkin, Yellow	
	109113	Square Ice	$10.95
		Lilac, Light Blue, Turquoise, Green	

FLEURETTES SHOWN AT 50%

FLOWERS SHOWN AT 50% IN OLD OLIVE

Flower Fusion

Custom colored felt flowers will add an eclectic dimension to any of your projects. 14 flower designs in 3 colors. More than 130 individual pieces packaged in a fun tin.

	110720	Flower Fusion	$14.95
		Pumpkin Pie, Rose Red, Old Olive	

Fleurettes II

Use these handmade, crocheted flowers to add a delicate touch to any project. Dye with our Classic ink to create flowers to coordinate with our exclusive colors. 12 flowers: 4 ea. of 3 flowers shown—1", 1-1/4", and 1-1/2".

	115604	Fleurettes II	$9.95
		Whisper White	

Stampin' Glitter

For the perfect amount of sparkle, try our different glitters. Apply with Heat & Stick powder, Tombow Multi Purpose Adhesive, Sticky Strip, Sticky Cuts, or a 2-Way Glue Pen, sold separately.

	102023	Dazzling Diamonds (1/2 oz.)	$4.50
	108797	Chunky Essentials (1 oz. ea.)	$15.95
		Red, White, Silver, Black	
	111343	Chunky Sprinkles	$15.95
		Light Pink, Light Blue, Celery, Crystal Iris	
	108796	Fine Cosmo (1/4 oz. ea.)	$13.95
		Rose Pink, Orchid, Light Blue, Celery, Turquoise	
	114286	Fine Galaxy (1/4 oz. ea.)	$13.95
		Black, Silver, Red, Gold, Champagne	
	114287	Fine Supernova (1/4 oz. ea.)	$13.95
		Chocolate, Olive, Orange, Pink, Aqua	

Heat & Stick Powder

Use this product to apply Stampin' Glitter to your stamped image with precision. Acid free. 1/2 oz.

	100625	Heat & Stick Powder	$4.50

Micro Beads

Try using Tombow Multi Purpose Adhesive, Sticky Strip, or Sticky Cuts to adhere these fun beads!

	104266	Micro Beads	$5.25

Bead Duo

Monochromatic bead assortments contain approx. 30 grams of colored micro beads and 30 grams of assorted hexagon and bugle beads, each packaged in a Stampin' Store mini container.

	110752	Pink Duo	$9.95
		(Clear Micro Beads)	
	110753	Blue Duo	$9.95
	110754	Green Duo	$9.95
	110732	Orange Duo	$9.95
	110731	Red Duo	$9.95
	110733	Silver Duo	$9.95

Apply larger beads to your project first, and use the coordinating micro beads to fill in the spaces. Use with Sticky Cuts, Sticky Strip, or Tombow Multi Purpose Adhesive.

Sticky Cuts Sweet

2 sheets of die-cut words and images. Use with our Stampin' Glitter or Bead Duos. 12" x 12".

	114301	Sticky Cuts Sweet	$8.95

Sticky Cuts Letters

Use with our Bead Duos or Stampin' Glitter to make personalizing your projects, gifts, and work spaces easy and fun. 2 sheets included. 12" x 12".

	111109	Sticky Cuts Letters	$8.95

Sticky Pages

Use sheets to cover On Board albums with Designer Series paper or create your own Sticky Cuts with the Big Shot. These are only two of the possibilities with these sticky sheets! See what you can create. Pkg. of 2. 12" x 12".

	114300	Sticky Pages	$6.95

Your projects will go from basic to beautiful with our exceptional embellishments. Choose from our Accents & Elements, buttons, tags, and more.

buttons and tags

Corduroy Buttons

Add texture to your projects using these custom-colored buttons and brads. 24 pieces: 8 ea. of button shown.

■	114339	Chocolate Chip	**$9.95**
■	114340	Kraft	**$9.95**
■	114342	Pumpkin Pie	**$9.95**
■	114343	Summer Sun	**$9.95**
■	114345	Basic Gray	**$9.95**

Clear Buttons

Dress up these buttons by applying Rub-On images or by stamping and attaching a cut-out shape to the button. 8 ea. in three sizes: 3/4" circle, 1" circle, and 1" square.

105447	Clear Buttons	**$4.95**

Metal Edge Tags

These fun tags are great to stamp on, or customize using vellum or Designer Series paper. Each package contains six 2" tags and six 1-1/2" tags. Shown at 40%.

103374	Aluminum White Circle	**$4.25**

PLAYGROUND

Designer Buttons

Includes 30 buttons, 3 ea. of button style shown.

ⓝ	■■■■	116313	Playground	**$7.95**
			Tempting Turquoise, Real Red, More Mustard, Old Olive	
ⓝ	■■■■	116312	Sherbet	**$7.95**
			Pretty in Pink, Certainly Celery, Bashful Blue, Pumpkin Pie	
	■■■■	114333	Button Latte	**$7.95**
			Chocolate Chip, So Saffron, Very Vanilla, Whisper White	

Colored Buttons

Hand-dyed to coordinate with a selection of our exclusive colors. Approx. 80 square and circle buttons in 2 sizes.

●●●●	107421	Fresh Favorites I	**$6.95**
		Apricot Appeal, Certainly Celery, Not Quite Navy, Tempting Turquoise	
●●●●	107422	Fresh Favorites II	**$6.95**
		Always Artichoke, Brocade Blue, Rose Red, So Saffron	

BUTTONS SHOWN AT 75% UNLESS OTHERWISE NOTED.
TAGS SHOWN AT 40%.

© 1990–2009 STAMPIN' UP! ACCESSORIES **181**

ribbon

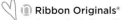

Ribbon Originals®

Approx. 9 yds: 3 ea. of 3 designs. 1/4", 1/2", and 5/8" wide.

	116232	Orchard	$9.95
		Elegant Eggplant, Always Artichoke, Sahara Sand, More Mustard, Very Vanilla	

Ribbon Originals

Approx. 9 yds: 3 ea. of 3 designs. 5/16", 5/8", and 7/8" wide.

	116230	Masterpiece	$9.95
		Close to Cocoa, Very Vanilla, Chocolate Chip, Certainly Celery	

Ribbon Originals

Approx. 9 yds: 3 ea. of 3 designs. 3/16", 3/8", and 7/8" wide.

	116231	Elementary	$9.95
		So Saffron, Whisper White, Old Olive, Not Quite Navy	

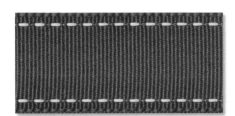

1" Double-Stitched Grosgrain Ribbon

Grosgrain ribbon features a double-stitched pattern; use alone or layer it with other ribbon. 1" wide, approx. 10 yds.

	115607	Real Red	$8.95
	111848	Bashful Blue	$8.95
	111849	Chocolate Chip	$8.95
	111846	Rose Red	$8.95

1/2" Striped Grosgrain Ribbon

Enjoy our classic grosgrain ribbon, available in this striped pattern. 1/2" wide, approx. 10 yds.

	110717	Bashful Blue	$7.95
	110715	Pumpkin Pie	$7.95
	110714	Real Red	$7.95
	113883	Old Olive	$7.95
	113882	Pretty in Pink	$7.95
	113699	So Saffron	$7.95

1/2" Polka-Dot Grosgrain Ribbon

This grosgrain ribbon features a fun polka-dot pattern. 1/2" wide, approx. 15 yds.

	115613	Rich Razzleberry	$9.95
	115610	Bermuda Bay	$9.95
	115612	Soft Suede	$9.95
	115614	Crushed Curry	$9.95
	115609	Dusty Durango	$9.95
	115611	Melon Mambo	$9.95

RIBBON SHOWN AT ACTUAL SIZE

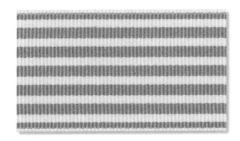

1-1/4" Striped Grosgrain Ribbon
This striped ribbon is the ideal width to tie around gifts, but you can also use it on any project. 1-1/4" wide, approx. 10 yds.

	115616	Pumpkin Pie	$8.95
	115617	Chocolate Chip	$8.95
	115618	Old Olive	$8.95
	115615	Basic Black	$8.95

3/4" Polka-Dot Grosgrain Ribbon
Our polka-dot grosgrain ribbon in a wider width perfect for gift wrapping and gift tags. 3/4" wide, approx. 10 yds.

	115608	Real Red	$8.95

5/8" Satin Ribbon
Give your project instant elegance with our satin ribbon. 5/8" wide, approx. 15 yards.

	114616	Whisper White	$8.95

Gingham Ribbon
Add a touch of nostalgia to your projects. 3/16" wide, approx. 15 yards.

	104832	Black	$7.50
	104827	Red	$7.50

1/4" Grosgrain Ribbon
High-quality exclusive ribbon gives your project the perfect touch. 1/4" wide, approx. 15 yards.

	109027	Basic Black	$4.95
	109025	Whisper White	$4.95
	109026	Very Vanilla	$4.95
	109030	Pumpkin Pie	$4.95
	109040	Apricot Appeal	$4.95
	109032	Pretty in Pink	$4.95
	109034	Real Red	$4.95
	111366	Rose Red	$4.95
	109028	Bravo Burgundy	$4.95
	109039	Elegant Eggplant	$4.95
	109036	Night of Navy	$4.95
	109038	Tempting Turquoise	$4.95
	109029	Bashful Blue	$4.95
	111369	Sage Shadow	$4.95
	109031	Certainly Celery	$4.95
	111368	Old Olive	$4.95
	109033	Mellow Moss	$4.95
	109035	Always Artichoke	$4.95
	111367	Chocolate Chip	$4.95

5/8" Grosgrain Ribbon
Wide grosgrain ribbon in many of our popular colors. 5/8" wide, approx. 15 yards.

	109055	Very Vanilla	$7.95
	109051	Chocolate Chip	$7.95
	109053	Bravo Burgundy	$7.95
	109052	Real Red	$7.95
	109056	Regal Rose	$7.95
	109057	Brocade Blue	$7.95
	109050	Certainly Celery	$7.95
	109054	Old Olive	$7.95
	115605	Basic Black	$7.95

Taffeta Ribbon
Timeless ribbon adds a touch of elegance to any project. 3/8" width approx. 10 yards.

	109070	Whisper White	$6.95
	109071	Very Vanilla	$6.95
	109068	Kraft	$6.95
	109065	Chocolate Chip	$6.95
	109064	Basic Gray	$6.95
	109069	Mellow Moss	$6.95
	109066	Bashful Blue	$6.95
	109067	Pretty in Pink	$6.95

Linen Thread
Diameter is fine enough for use with buttons or with needles. Approx. 15 yards.

	104199	Linen Thread	$4.50

Hemp Twine
Approx. 12 yards.

	100982	Natural	$2.95

Organza Ribbon
Add graceful delicacy to your projects with this Whisper White organza ribbon. 5/8" wide, approx 15 yds.

	114319	Whisper White	$5.95

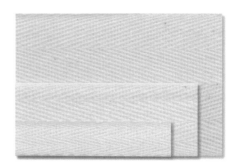

Twill Tape
Use alone or create a custom look with our stamps or Rub-Ons. 100%-cotton twill tape can be dyed with our Classic refills. Approx. 9 yards: 3 yards ea. of 3/8-inch, 3/4-inch, and 1-1/2-inch twill.

105245	Twill Tape	$5.95

Create custom chipboard for all your projects by decorating it with Designer Series paper or card stock.

1. Glue the paper to the chipboard piece. 2. Cut around the chipboard piece. 3. Sand the edges.

on board

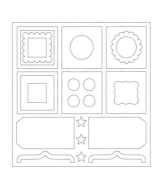

On Board Essentials

Essential pieces highlight cards, scrapbook pages, and other crafting projects. Assortment includes three 12" x 12" sheets: 1 ea. of 3 designs. More than 150 images included.

| 112085 | Essentials | $12.95 |

On Board Loads of Letters

Multiple letters in three font styles make it easy to create words. Assortment includes three 12" x 12" sheets: 1 ea. of 3 designs.

| 112084 | Loads of Letters | $12.95 |

On Board Journals

Art Journal includes 50 sheets of unlined, acid-free paper. Approx. journal dimensions: 5-3/4" x 8-3/4". 5" x 5" Art Journal includes 20 sheets of Very Vanilla card stock. Approx. cover dimensions: 5-1/4" x 5-1/4".

| 107065 | Art Journal | $9.50 |
| 108495 | 5" x 5" Art Journal | $6.95 |

On Board So Tweet

Assortment coordinates with Sunny Day Simply Scrappin' and includes six 9" x 9" sheets. More than 80 images included.

| 113893 | So Tweet | $14.95 |

On Board Clipboards

Customize with Designer Series paper to create seasonal photo holders, wish lists, or reminders. Sized exclusively for Stampin' Up!

| 109192 | 13" x 7-1/2" | $15.95 |
| 109191 | 4-1/2" x 9" | $6.50 |

On Board Book Basics

Use our thick chipboard to create personalized albums. Bind the covers with book clips, ribbon, or anything your heart desires! Long Board is sized and designed to use with the Sizzix Big Shot (page 194).

110713	Book Basics Large (4 pieces) 9-3/8" x 9-3/8"	$7.95
110712	Book Basics Small (4 pieces) 5" x 7-1/2"	$5.95
114320	Long Board (6 pieces) 5-3/4" x 13-3/4"	$6.95

On Board Batch of Blooms

Assortment includes six 9" x 9" sheets: 1 ea. of 6 designs with more than 200 images included.

| 112087 | Batch of Blooms | $14.95 |

On Board Album

Larger 3-ring, chipboard album includes 10 8-1/2" x 8-1/2" page protectors. Cover size: 9-1/2" x 11-1/4".

| 112456 | Ring Album 8-1/2" x 8-1/2" | $13.95 |
| 112455 | Ring Page Protectors (10) 8-1/2" x 8-1/2" | $5.95 |

On Board Timeless Type

Pieces include uppercase and lowercase alphabet as well as numbers. Multiple letters make it easy to create words. Assortment includes three 12" x 12" sheets: 1 ea. of 3 designs.

| 112083 | Timeless Type | $12.95 |

On Board Lots of Letters

Assortment includes three 12" x 12" sheets with almost 200 letters, numbers, and accents.

| 109182 | Lots of Letters | $12.95 |

Handheld Punches

1.	101227	1/16" Circle	$8.95

Punches

2.	112004	1-3/4" Circle	$15.95
3.	104401	1-3/8" Circle	$15.95
4.	104403	1-1/4" Circle	$15.95
5.	109046	1" Circle	$10.95
6.	107217	3/4" Circle	$10.95
7.	104390	1/2" Circle	$5.95
8.	105934	Tag	$15.95
9.	108264	Small Tag	$15.95
10.	107304	Small Oval	$15.95
11.	107305	Large Oval	$15.95
12.	112082	Wide Oval	$15.95
13.	109183	Trio Flower	$15.95
14.	104400	1-1/4" Square	$15.95
15.	103375	1-3/8" Square	$15.95
16.	109042	Photo Corners	$15.95
17.	107215	Tag Corner	$6.95
18.	107214	Ticket Corner	$6.95
19.	109047	3/16" Corner Rounder	$6.95
20.	109041	5-Petal Flower	$15.95
21.	110711	Boho Blossoms	$15.95
22.	108340	Round Tab	$15.95
23.	112208	Curly Label	$15.95
24.	116630	Modern Label	$15.95
25.	107590	Designer Label	$15.95
26.	105090	Word Window	$15.95
27.	113693	Full Heart	$15.95
28.	113694	Heart to Heart	$15.95
29.	110709	My Way	$15.95
30.	116628	Jumbo Snowflake*	$15.95
31.	116629	Butterfly	$15.95
32.	108341	Spiral	$10.95
33.	105088	Double Rectangle	$5.95
34.	109043	Scallop Circle	$15.95
35.	112081	Scallop Square	$15.95
36.	114889	Scallop Oval	$15.95
37.	112091	Scallop Edge	$15.95
38.	113692	Eyelet Border	$15.95
39.	110710	Large Star	$15.95
40.	109045	Star	$10.95
41.	105089	Horizontal Slot	$5.95
42.	104388	Slit	$5.95

*DUE TO THE INTRICACY OF THE DESIGN, THIS PUNCH MAY REQUIRE MORE PRESSURE TO PUNCH.

The Tearing Edge

Create natural-looking torn edges with precision. Approx. 13" x 1-1/2".

| 102930 | The Tearing Edge® | $19.95 |

Bone Folder

Use to score paper and make crisp folds.

| 102300 | Bone Folder | $6.95 |

Stampin' Emboss Powder

Our embossing powder meets all of your embossing needs. Try embossing several layers to achieve a thick, dimensional look. 1/2 oz.

109133	Black	$4.75
109132	White	$4.75
109129	Gold	$4.75
109131	Silver	$4.75
109130	Clear	$4.75
101930	Iridescent Ice	$4.75
100477	Glassy Glaze Enamel (1 oz.)	$4.75

Light Table

Our light table features a stainless steel frame, thick plexiglass top, tilt-up device, and bright, even light. This gives you the perfect surface for use with our Classy Brass templates. 10" x 12" work area.

| 102888 | Light Table | $49.95 |

Empressor Stylus

Dual-tipped, roller-ball embossing tool features comfort grips and works with any template. Smooth-rolling action reduces paper tearing. Small tip is perfect for small patterns and lightweight papers; large tip works great on card stock.

| 100716 | Empressor® Stylus | $10.95 |

Sanding Blocks

Use to distress the surface of your paper or to sand a rough edge.

| 103301 | Sanding Blocks (2) | $3.50 |

Crimper

Crimps card stock and paper up to 6-1/2" wide.

| 101618 | Crimper | $19.95 |

Heat & Stick Powder

Use this product to apply Stampin' Glitter to your stamped image with precision. Acid free. 1/2 oz.

| 100625 | Heat & Stick Powder | $4.50 |

Heat Tool

Use this electric heat tool with embossing powders, Heat & Stick Powder, and to heat-set pigment ink.

| 100005 | Heat Tool | $29.95 |

Powder Pals

Keep your work area neat and save glitters and powders with these terrific tools. Comes with 2 trays and a brush for clean up.

| 102197 | Powder Pals® | $19.95 |

Embossing Buddy

Rub across paper to reduce static. Use before embossing or applying glitter.

| 103083 | Embossing Buddy® | $5.95 |

Stylus

Use small tip for lightweight papers and large tip for card stock.

| 100663 | Stylus | $2.50 |

Classy Brass Templates

All Classy Brass® templates feature exclusive designs that coordinate with popular Stampin' Up! sets. Most templates also include convenient guides for paper piercing.

109542	Pick a Petal Coordinates with Pick a Petal (page 120)	$21.95
109539	Punches Plus Coordinates with punches (page 186)	$20.95
109541	Priceless Coordinates with Priceless (page 130)	$15.95
111807	Floral Frenzy Coordinates with Eastern Blooms (page 108)	$15.95
107412	Seeing Spots	$9.95
109540	Dots	$15.95

PICK A PETAL

PUNCHES PLUS

PRICELESS

FLORAL FRENZY

SEEING SPOTS

DOTS

Our Stampin' Around wheels are available in dozens of designs, many of which coordinate with our stamp sets. Use them together to make unique creations.

stampin' around.

Stampin' Around Handles
Does not include cartridge or wheel. Ink cartridges are sold on pages 155–157.

| 102971 | Stampin' Around Handle | **$3.95** |
| 103661 | Stampin' Around Jumbo Handle | **$5.95** |

Stampin' Around Wheel Storage
Each standard container stores 10 wheels; jumbo container stores 6 wheels.

| 105743 | Standard (2) | **$6.95** |
| 105741 | Jumbo (2) | **$6.95** |

Uninked Cartridges
These cartridges come uninked, ready to create your own cartridge with any of our Classic ink refills.

| 101529 | Cartridge | **$5.25** |
| 103678 | Jumbo Cartridge | **$7.50** |

Stampin' Around Wheel Guide
Wheel perfect background papers, borders, or mitered corners without worrying about crooked lines or overlapping images with this handy tool. Rubber feet keep the guide from moving or slipping. The guide can be configured for both standard and jumbo wheels.

| 104834 | Wheel Guide | **$9.95** |

Look for this symbol marking our Stampin' Around wheels throughout the catalog. Ink cartridges are sold on pages 155–157.

PRODUCTS SHOWN IN ALL STORAGE ITEMS ON THIS PAGE NOT INCLUDED.

© 1990–2009 STAMPIN' UP! **ACCESSORIES** **189**

Opportunity knocked, and YOU answered.

The key to completing any project is having the right set of tools. On these two pages, you'll find tools to help with cutting, tearing, measuring, folding, and more.

coloring and cleaning

Encore!® Pads

Add a rich, metallic look to your stamped projects with these acid-free, fade-resistant pigment ink pads. Metallic inks should be heat set when used in a scrapbook. These inks come in stackable, easy-to-hold pads. *sm*

	101017	Gold Pad	$8.95
	101242	Gold Refill (1/2 oz.)	$4.25
	101039	Silver Pad	$8.95
	102124	Silver Refill (1/2 oz.)	$4.25

uni-ball® Signo Gel Pen

The smooth-rolling ink of this gel pen allows you to add text or creative touches on dark card stock. Medium ballpoint tip. *sm*

105021	White	$3.95

Stampin' Write Journaler

Fade-resistant, waterproof, pigment markers ideal for journaling and scrapbooking. Tip sizes: .6mm and 2.3 mm bullet. *sm*

105394	Basic Black	$3.25

VersaMark

Create a tone-on-tone or a watermark effect with this pad and marker. Acid free. *sm*

102283	VersaMark® Pad	$7.50
102193	VersaMark Pad Refill (1/2 oz.)	$3.95
100901	VersaMarker	$3.25

StāzOn® Ink Pads

This quick-drying, permanent ink works great on nonporous surfaces. Use it to stamp an image before watercoloring.

■	101406	Jet Black Pad	$7.95
■	102566	Jet Black Refill (1/2 oz.)	$4.95
□	106960	White Pad & Refill (1/2 oz.)	$11.95

StāzOn Cleaner

StāzOn stamp cleaner is especially formulated to clean and condition stamps after use with StāzOn ink. This cleaner is used to prevent staining that can occur when using solvent-based inks.

109196	Cleaner (2 oz.)	$4.95

Stampin' Mist Stamp Cleaner

Lightly scented spray cleans and conditions your rubber stamps. For best results, clean stamp immediately after use.

102394	Stampin' Mist® (2 oz.)	$4.50
101022	Stampin' Mist Refill (8 oz.)	$9.50

Stampin' Scrub

Dual-sided tray contains replaceable black fiber scrubbing pads. Clean stamp on one side, blot dry on the other. Sized to fit even our largest stamps. Each pad is approx. 7" x 5-3/4".

102642	Stampin' Scrub®	$16.95
101230	Stampin' Scrub Refill Pads (2)	$9.95

Circle Scissor Plus

Making perfect circles has never been simpler! Use the Circle Scissor® Plus to cut and draw circles with ease. Works best with the Glass Mat. Replacement blades are sold separately in a pkg. of 3.

112530	Circle Scissor Plus	**$29.95**
112532	Replacement Blades	**$3.95**

Glass Mat

Mat provides a smooth glass cutting surface that allows a cutting blade to glide without dragging or skipping. Use with the Circle Scissor Plus. 13" x 13".

112531	Glass Mat	**$19.95**

Paper Cutter

Cuts paper up to 12". Features easy-to-read grid lines and black base. Measures widths up to 15-1/2". Comes with 2 cutting blades. Refills include either a cutting and scoring blade or 2 cutting blades.

104152	Paper Cutter	**$24.95**
104154	Cutting & Scoring Blade Refills	**$5.95**
104153	Cutting Blade Refills	**$5.95**

Craft & Rubber Scissors

Use these sharp, short-bladed crafting scissors to cut twine, thread, rubber, Texture Cuts Wood Sheets, wood, wire, and other materials. 1-3/4" blade length.

103179	Craft & Rubber Scissors	**$19.95**

Paper Snips

These small, thin-bladed scissors provide expert cutting in even the tiniest of areas, and the precision-ground tips allow you to cut to the end of the blade. 2-1/2" blade length.

103579	Paper Snips	**$9.95**

Craft & Paper Scissors

High-quality, multipurpose crafting scissors create clean, crisp cuts on ribbon, paper, card stock, and more. 3-3/4" blade length with an ergonomic handle.

108360	Craft & Paper Scissors	**$29.95**

Hobby Blade

Extra sharp, with 5 refill blades. Comes in a convenient storage tube.

102449	Hobby Blade & Refills	**$4.50**

Cutting Mat

This no-slip mat allows for safe cutting while protecting your work surface. Grid lines provide a guide for precise cutting with your hobby blade every time. 12" x 18".

101087	Cutting Mat	**$15.95**

Paper-Piercing Tool

Use the paper-piercing tool to embellish any crafting project. Comes with reusable storage tube and protective cap. Handle length: 3-1/2"; length of piercing tip: 3/4".

116631	Paper Piercing Tool	**$3.50**

Mat Pack

Paper-piercing pad, paper-piercing template, and setting mat, each 4" x 4".

105826	Mat Pack	**$9.95**

Tabletop Paper Cutter

Precise paper cutter features stainless-steel precision-ground blades and is ideal for card making and scrapbooking.

106959	Tabletop Paper Cutter	**$45.95**

Grid Paper

Oversized pad of paper protects your stamping work surfaces. Serves as scratch paper and makes cleanup a snap! Features include a standard card-dimension list and space for writing a wish list.

102787	Grid Paper (100 sheets)	**$9.95**

Cutter Kit

Use this convenient and portable cutter kit for all of your projects on the go! Includes rotary cutter, perforating tool, scoring tool, and a 7-sided distressing tool.

106958	Cutter Kit	**$16.95**

Crop-A-Dile

Circle punch through chipboard, tin, and multiple paper layers with ease. Its built-in 1/8" and 3/16" eyelet setters easily set eyelets of both sizes.

108362	Crop-A-Dile™	**$29.95**

Stamp-a-ma-jig

Use this stamp positioner for precise stamp alignment every time. Nonskid base. Includes reusable, wipe-clean imaging sheet for easy placement.

101049	Stamp-a-ma-jig®	**$11.95**

Pencil Sharpener

Sharp steel blade creates a fine point with 2 sizes that accommodate Stampin' Up! Watercolor Pencils and crayons. Removable receptacle for shavings keeps things neat.

100745	Pencil Sharpener	**$4.95**

applicators

Color Spritzer Tool
Achieve spectacular effects using a Stampin' Write marker with this convenient tool. The tool mists the ink from the marker to create a spattered look. Marker not included.

| 107066 | Color Spritzer Tool | **$12.95** |

Brayer
Use for special-effect backgrounds and uniform inking on large stamps. Includes handle and soft rubber attachment.

| 102395 | Handle with Rubber Attachment | **$12.50** |

Stamping Sponges

| 101610 | Stamping Sponges (3) | **$3.50** |

Sponge Daubers

| 102892 | Sponge Daubers (12) | **$10.95** |

Aqua Painter
Use this versatile tool for controlled watercoloring. It's less messy and more transportable than a cup and watercolor brush. To use, fill reservoir with water. (1 medium and 1 large per pkg.)

| 103954 | Aqua Painter | **$16.95** |

Blender Pens
2 brush tips on each. Use with Watercolor pencils, Watercolor Wonder Crayons, Classic Stampin' Pads, ink refills, and Stampin' Pastels to blend color. Acid free and xylene free. 3 per pkg.

| 102845 | Blender Pens (3) | **$9.95** |

adhesives

2-Way Glue Pen
This adhesive is temporary when allowed to dry before adhering or permanent when adhered promptly. Use to adhere glitter. Acid free. 10 grams.

| 100425 | 2-Way Glue Pen | **$3.50** |

Dotto
Tiny repositionable adhesive dots in a convenient dispenser. Acid free. 585". *sm*

| 103305 | Dotto® | **$12.95** |
| 100902 | Dotto Refill | **$6.50** |

SNAIL Adhesive
Double-sided, permamnent adhesive dispensed continuously. Acid free. 472". *sm*

| 104332 | SNAIL Adhesive® | **$6.95** |
| 104331 | SNAIL Refill | **$4.50** |

Sticky Strip
Use this double-sided, extra-tacky strip to adhere micro beads or ribbon and make three-dimensional items stick tightly. Acid free. Approx. 1/4" wide, approx. 10 yds.

| 104294 | Sticky Strip | **$6.95** |

Glue Dots
Glue Dots® are a super-sticky adhesive designed for use on three-dimensional accents. No fumes, no mess, no drying time required. Acid free.

103683	Mini Glue Dots	**$4.95**
	Approx 3/16" dia., 300 dots.	
104183	Pop-Up Glue Dots	**$3.95**
	Approx 1/2" dia., 1/8" thick. 75 dots.	

Crystal Effects
Add a dimensional, lacquered look to any stamped image. Acid free. 2 oz.

| 101055 | Crystal Effects® | **$6.25** |

Stampin' Dimensionals
1/16" thick double-sided, adhesive foam dots. Acid free.

| 104430 | Stampin' Dimensionals (300) | **$3.95** |

Adhesive Remover
This adhesive remover works like an eraser. Note: It does not remove tape. 2" x 2"

| 103684 | Adhesive Remover | **$3.50** |

Anywhere Glue Stick
Rectangle shape allows you access to the corners of your project. Acid free. 20 grams each.

| 104045 | Anywhere Glue Stick (2) | **$3.95** |

Tombow Multi Purpose Adhesive
This adhesive is temporary when allowed to momentarily dry before adhering or permanent when adhered promptly. Use it with beads and glitter or to secure Designer Series paper to chipboard. Acid free. .875 oz.

| 110755 | Tombow® Adhesive | **$3.95** |

Let our artwork enhance your surroundings. With our vinyl Décor Elements, you have a variety of options for giving your home a new look without the high price of repainting and redecorating.

Go confidently in the direction of your dreams.
- Henry David Thoreau

décor elements

Tree, Thoughts & Prayers*

BLACK	CHOCOLATE			
116008	116002	Tree, Thoughts & Prayers (S) 18-5/8" x 13"		$12.95
116009	116003	Tree, Thoughts & Prayers (M) 34-3/4" x 24-3/8"		$23.95
116010	116004	Tree, Thoughts & Prayers (L) 52-1/8" x 36-1/8"		$35.95

Spooky Brocade

BLACK	DARK GRAY	OLIVE	PUMPKIN PIE		
117572	117935	117936	117937	Spooky Brocade (S) 8" x 6-7/8"	$8.95
117938	117939	117940	117941	Spooky Brocade (L) 13" x 12-3/4"	$17.95

Vintage Ornaments (SET OF 4 PLUS EXTENDER LINES)

BLACK	CHOCOLATE	REAL RED	WHITE		
117578	117966	117967	117968	Vintage Ornaments (S) LARGEST ORNAMENT: 5-1/4" x 8-7/8"	$16.95
117969	117970	117971	117972	Vintage Ornaments (M) LARGEST ORNAMENT: 7-3/8" x 12-1/2"	$19.95

BABY

Baby Blossoms

CHOCOLATE	CERTAINLY CELERY	PRETTY IN PINK	SO SAFRON	WHITE		
117512	117769	117770	117771	117772	Baby Blossoms (S) 6-1/4" x 6-7/8"	$8.95
117773	117774	117775	117776	117777	Baby Blossoms (M) 11-7/8" x 13"	$14.95

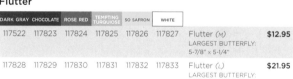

Flutter

DARK GRAY	CHOCOLATE	ROSE RED	TEMPTING TURQUOISE	SO SAFRON	WHITE		
117522	117823	117824	117825	117826	117827	Flutter (M) LARGEST BUTTERFLY: 5-7/8" x 5-1/4"	$12.95
117828	117829	117830	117831	117832	117833	Flutter (L) LARGEST BUTTERFLY: 9-3/4" x 9-1/8"	$21.95

in·spire : {in-spīr} *v.*
To cause or create new ideas.
Fresh thought; to influence.
To motivate one to action.

Inspire Definition

BLACK	CHOCOLATE	WHITE		
117523	117834	117835	Inspire Definition (M) 20" x 7-3/8"	$16.95
117836	117837	117838	Inspire Definition (L) 29-1/5" x 10-7/8"	$21.95

Décor Elements Applicator

Apply Décor Elements designs with this convenient angled plastic applicator. Handy for both applying & removing. Approx. 2-7/8" x 2-1/4".

114285	Applicator	$1.95

To see our full line and other Definitely Decorative products, ask your demonstrator or go online to www.stampinup.com.

Stampin' Up! is pleased to team up with Sizzix to offer you a multipurpose die-cutting system! The Big Shot works with card stock, Designer Series paper, fabric, chipboard, plastic, and more. With this machine, your projects will come together in seconds!

Sizzix Big Shot

Big Shot Die-Cut Machine

With the Big Shot®, you can create die cuts with any of our exclusive Stampin' Up! dies—or any Sizzix® die. Machine includes standard cutting pads and multipurpose platform so you can start cutting immediately.

| 113439 | Big Shot Die-Cut Machine | **$99.95** |

Doctor's Bag

This bag features Stampin' Up!'s logo and is sized to hold the Big Shot die-cut machine, cutting pad, and dies for convenient storage and transport.

| 113474 | Doctor's Bag | **$69.95** |

Decorative Strip Spacer Platform

Along with Decorative Strip cutting pads (sold separately), the Decorative Strip Spacer Platform is required to use Decorative Strip dies in the Big Shot die-cut machine.

| 113477 | Decorative Strip Spacer Platform | **$9.95** |

Decorative Strip Cutting Pads

Along with the Decorative Strip Spacer Platform (sold separately), these pads accommodate the extra-long format of Decorative Strip dies. Includes 1 pair. 13" long.

| 113479 | Decorative Strip Cutting Pads | **$7.95** |

Standard Replacement Cutting Pads

Essential for cutting with the Bigz™, Originals™, and Sizzlits™ dies, the replacement cutting pads can be flipped over for twice the wear. Includes 1 pair.

| 113475 | Standard Replacement Cutting Pads | **$8.95** |

Extended Cutting Pads

Essential for cutting with the Bigz XL dies, the cutting pads can be flipped over for twice the wear. Includes 1 pair.

| 113478 | Extended Cutting Pads | **$19.95** |

Extended Premium Crease Pad

Use the extended premium crease pad with the Big Shot machine to create subtle fold lines for Bigz XL cards, envelopes, bags, boxes, and pockets.

| 117630 | Extended Premium Crease Pad | **$19.95** |

Standard Premium Crease Pad

Use this pad in the Big Shot die-cut machine to create subtle fold lines for Bigz and Originals cards, envelopes, bags, boxes, and pockets.

| 113476 | Standard Premium Crease Pad | **$8.95** |

Standard Texturz Impressions Pad

Use with Silicone Rubber, Texturz™ Plates, and Multipurpose Platform to provide subtle, detailed backgrounds.

| 114614 | Standard Texturz Impressions Pad | **$5.95** |

Standard Texturz Silicone Rubber

Use with Impressions Pad, Texturz Texture Plates, and Multipurpose Platform to provide soft, subtle backgrounds.

| 114615 | Standard Texturz Silicone Rubber | **$5.95** |

embosslits dies

STAMPIN' UP! HI   STAMPIN' UP! THANKS   STAMPIN' UP! SWEETEST STEM

STAMPIN' UP! SIMPLE FLOWER   STAMPIN' UP! CHERRY BLOSSOM   STAMPIN' UP! FLOWER BURST

Embosslits Dies

Embosslits dies measure 2-1/4" x 2-1/2". These chemically etched dies include a positive and negative image that allows simultaneous cutting and embossing. Embosslits cut through card stock and Designer Series paper. Use them with Standard Cutting Pads and the Multipurpose Platform (sold separately).

	115952	Stampin' Up! Hi	$11.95
	115957	Stampin' Up! Thanks	$11.95
	114513	Stampin' Up! Sweetest Stem	$11.95
	114514	Stampin' Up! Simple Flower	$11.95
	114516	Stampin' Up! Cherry Blossom	$11.95
	114515	Stampin' Up! Flower Burst	$11.95

textured impressions embossing folders

STAMPIN' UP! ELEGANT BOUQUET   STAMPIN' UP! FINIAL PRESS   STAMPIN' UP! MANHATTAN FLOWER

Textured Impressions Embossing Folders

Textured Impressions Embossing Folders measure 4-1/2" x 5-3/4". These folders create a strong embossed image sized for the front of a standard card. Use them with the Standard Cutting Pads and Multipurpose Platform (sold seperately).

	115964	Stampin' Up! Elegant Bouquet	$7.95
	115963	Stampin' Up! Finial Press	$7.95
	114517	Stampin' Up! Manhattan Flower	$7.95

texturz plates

STAMPIN' UP! PERFECT DETAILS

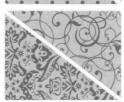

TEXTURE PLATES KIT #4   STAMPIN' UP! BACKGROUNDS 1

Texturz Plates

Texturz plates measure 8" x 5-7/8" and create subtle patterns and designs on card stock, giving your project a delicate embossed background. Set of 3 double-sided plates offer 6 unique and exciting options. Use with the Multipurpose Platform, Impressions Pad, and Silicone Rubber (sold separately).

	115962	Stampin' Up! Perfect Details	$3.95
	114531	Texture Plates Kit #4	$9.95
	114512	Stampin' Up! Backgrounds 1	$11.95

EMBOSSLITS DIES SHOWN AT 35%; TEXTURED IMPRESSIONS DIES SHOWN AT 30%; TEXTURZ PLATES SHOWN AT 20%
STAMPIN' UP! EXCLUSIVE ▢ CUT ▬ SCORE ▬ PERFORATION ----

Sizzlits Dies

Sizzlits dies measure 2-1/4" x 2-1/2". These chemically etched dies cut through single layers of card stock and Designer Series paper. Use them with Standard Cutting Pads and the Multipurpose Platform (sold separately).

	115974	Stampin' Up! Curves Ahead	$5.50
	115973	Stampin' Up! Joyful	$5.50
	115972	Stampin' Up! Many Thanks	$5.50
	115969	Stampin' Up! Floral Fusion	$5.50
	114511	Stampin' Up! Little Leaves	$5.50
	113441	Swirls Scribbles	$4.95
	114530	Flower Blossom	$4.95
	113440	Buttons #5	$4.95
	113445	Pumpkin Faces	$4.95
	113443	Pumpkin #4	$4.95
	113442	Daisy Flower	$4.95
	113444	Sparkle	$4.95

STAMPIN' UP! CURVES AHEAD

STAMPIN' UP! JOYFUL

STAMPIN' UP! MANY THANKS

STAMPIN' UP! FLORAL FUSION

STAMPIN' UP! LITTLE LEAVES

SWIRLS SCRIBBLES

FLOWER BLOSSOM

BUTTONS #5

PUMPKIN FACES

PUMPKIN #4

DAISY FLOWER

SPARKLE

Sizzlits Decorative Strip Dies

Sizzlits Decorative Strips measure 2-3/8" x 12-5/8". These chemically etched dies cut through card stock and Designer Series paper. Use them with the Extended Spacer Platform and Decorative Strip Cutting Pads (sold separately).

113452	Stampin' Up! Join in the Cheer	$21.95
114510	Stampin' Up! Billboard	$21.95
114529	Birds & Branches	$19.95
113456	Swirly	$19.95
113455	Loopy Flowers	$19.95
113453	Naturally Serif	$19.95
113454	Flowers	$19.95

BIRDS & BRANCHES

SWIRLY

LOOPY FLOWERS

STAMPIN' UP! JOIN IN THE CHEER

NATURALLY SERIF

STAMPIN' UP! BILLBOARD

FLOWERS

SIZZLITS, AND SIZZLIT DECORATIVE STRIP DIES SHOWN AT 30%

Try our versatile Sizzlits dies. Each one includes a variety of coordinating images designed to enhance your projects.

medium sizzlits dies

STAMPIN' UP! TIMELESS TYPE ALPHABET JUNIOR (SET OF 12) LETTERS AND NUMBERS ARE APPROX. 1" x 1"

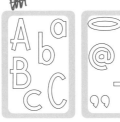

GO GO BOOTS ALPHABET (SET OF 12) LETTERS AND NUMBERS ARE APPROX. 1-1/8" x 1-1/8"

Medium Sizzlits Dies

Medium Sizzlits dies measure 3-3/4" x 2-1/2". These chemically etched dies cut through single layers of card stock and Designer Series paper. Use them with Standard Cutting Pads and Multipurpose Platform (sold separately). Comes in a storage box.

115951	Stampin' Up! Timeless Type Junior Alphabet (set of 12)	**$74.95**
113450	Go Go Boots Alphabet (set of 12)	**$69.95**

sizzlits 4-pack dies

Sizzlits 4-Pack Dies

Sizzlits dies (set of 4) measure 2-1/4" x 2-1/2". These chemically etched dies cut through card stock and Designer Series paper. Use them with Standard Cutting Pads and Multipurpose Platform (sold separately).

114508	Stampin' Up! Lots of Tags	**$21.95**
114509	Stampin' Up! Big Bold Cupcakes	**$21.95**
113485	Stampin' Up! Birds & Blooms	**$21.95**
113447	Spring Flowers Set	**$19.95**
113448	Hearts Set	**$19.95**
113449	Snowflakes #2 Set	**$19.95**
113446	Build a Flower Set #2	**$19.95**

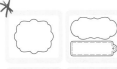

STAMPIN' UP! LOTS OF TAGS

STAMPIN' UP! BIG BOLD CUPCAKES

STAMPIN' UP! BIRDS & BLOOMS

SPRING FLOWERS SET

HEARTS SET

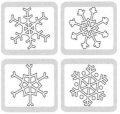

SNOWFLAKES SET #2

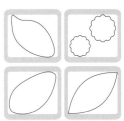

BUILD A FLOWER SET #2

MEDIUM SIZZLITS AND SIZZLITS 4-PACK DIES SHOWN AT 30%

STAMPIN' UP! EXCLUSIVE ▪ CUT ── SCORE ── PERFORATION ----

ACCESSORIES

The Bigz dies are rule-based dies measuring 5-1/2" x 6" that cut through various materials such as wood sheets, window sheets, and vellum. Use them with Standard Cutting Pads (sold separately). Clear-based dies offer easy positioning, which allows even more personalization on your project.

bigz dies

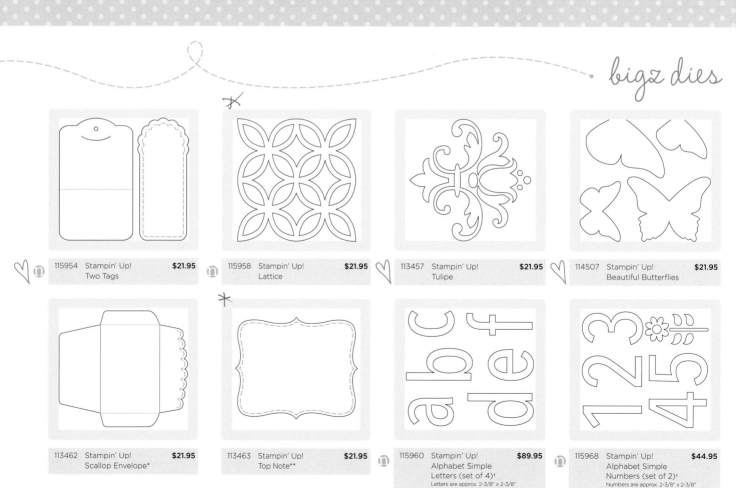

115954	Stampin' Up! Two Tags	$21.95
115958	Stampin' Up! Lattice	$21.95
113457	Stampin' Up! Tulipe	$21.95
114507	Stampin' Up! Beautiful Butterflies	$21.95

113462	Stampin' Up! Scallop Envelope*	$21.95
113463	Stampin' Up! Top Note**	$21.95
115960	Stampin' Up! Alphabet Simple Letters (set of 4)†	$89.95
	Letters are approx. 2-3/8" x 2-3/8"	
115968	Stampin' Up! Alphabet Simple Numbers (set of 2)†	$44.95
	Numbers are approx. 2-3/8" x 2-3/8"	

BIGZ DIES SHOWN AT 25%
†ALPHABET SIMPLE LETTERS USES "B" AS "D," "P," AND "Q" AS WELL AS "N" AS "U." ALPHABET SIMPLE NUMBERS USES "6" AS "9"

113466	Pillow Box*	$19.95
113468	Scallop Circle	$19.95
113469	Scallop Circle #2	$19.95
113470	Flower Layers w/Leaf	$19.95

114521	Frame, Oval Scallop	$19.95
114520	Flower, Daisies #2	$19.95
113473	5-Point 3D Star*	$19.95
114524	Fringed Flower	$19.95

114523	Decorative Accents	$19.95
113467	Petal Card*	$19.95
113471	Build a Flower	$19.95
113472	Circle 3D Ornament*	$19.95

113464	Serif Essentials Alphabet (set of 7) Letters are approx. 2" x 2"	$149.95
113465	Bird w/Leaves and Flower	$19.95
114522	Decorative Accent #2	$19.95

bigz clear dies

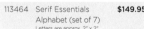

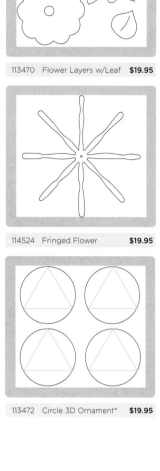

115950	Stampin' Up! Scallop Square	$21.95
114532	Card, Telephone & Address	$19.95
114533	Clear Circle	$19.95
114534	Flower	$19.95

*WORKS BEST WITH THE PREMIUM CREASE PAD, USING ONLY ONE LAYER OF MATERIAL AT A TIME
**WORKS BEST USING ONLY ONE LAYER OF MATERIAL AT A TIME

STAMPIN' UP! EXCLUSIVE   CUT ——   SCORE ——   PERFORATION ----

The Bigz XL dies are rule-based dies measuring 6" x 13-3/4" that cut through various materials such as wood sheets, window sheets, and vellum. These dies also work with our chipboard (page 185) when your project needs a sturdy backing or base. Use Bigz XL dies with Extended Cutting Pads to create boxes, bags, pennants, envelopes, and more!

bigz xl dies

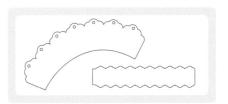

115961   Stampin' Up! Perfect Setting   **$42.95**

113484   Stampin' Up! Baskets & Blooms*   **$39.95**

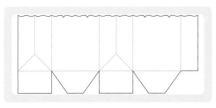

115965   Stampin' Up! Fancy Favor*   **$39.95**

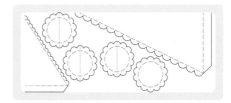

113483   Stampin' Up! Pennant*   **$39.95**

BIGX XL DIES SHOWN AT 17%
*WORKS BEST WITH THE EXTENDED PREMIUM CREASE PAD, USING ONLY ONE LAYER OF MATERIAL AT A TIME

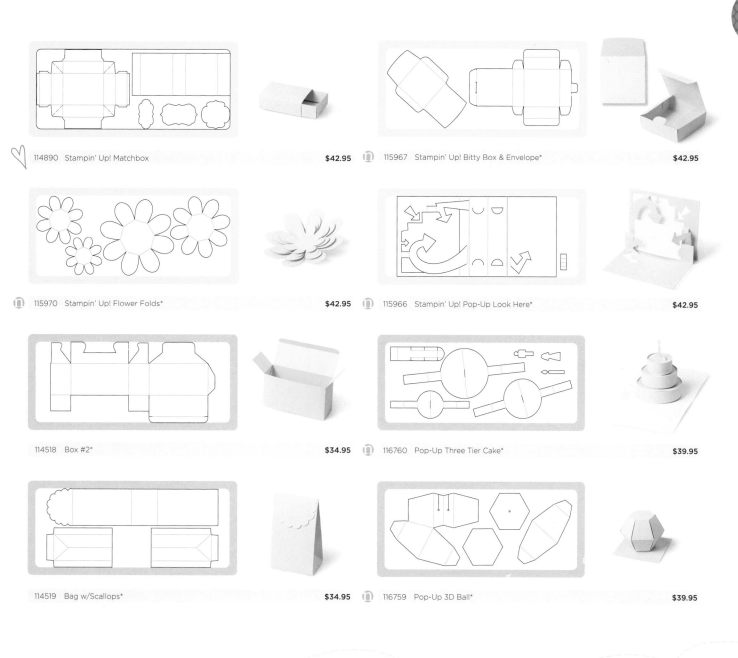

114890   Stampin' Up! Matchbox   **$42.95**

115967   Stampin' Up! Bitty Box & Envelope*   **$42.95**

115970   Stampin' Up! Flower Folds*   **$42.95**

115966   Stampin' Up! Pop-Up Look Here*   **$42.95**

114518   Box #2*   **$34.95**

116760   Pop-Up Three Tier Cake*   **$39.95**

114519   Bag w/Scallops*   **$34.95**

116759   Pop-Up 3D Ball*   **$39.95**

movers & shapers

MOVABLE PIECE

MOVABLE PIECES

Movers & Shapers

The exclusive Curly Label Bigz die is designed to coordinate with the Curly Label punch (page 186). Use the coordinating die and punch to create exciting and unified projects.

114506   Stampin' Up! Movers & Shapers Curly Label*   **$42.95**

Magnetic Movers & Shapers

The Punch Windows Movers dies measure 2-5/16" x 2-7/16". The cut images are slightly larger than the coordinating punch shapes. Use with Extended Cutting Pads. Note: Must be used inside the Curly Label die to achieve a proper cut.

115953   Stampin' Up! Punch Windows (set of 4)*   **$29.95**

*MOVABLE PIECES COORDINATE WITH OUR PUNCHES (PAGE 186).

STAMPIN' UP! EXCLUSIVE   CUT ——   SCORE ———   PERFORATION - - - -   MOVABLE AREA

The Originals dies are perfectly sized for use on card fronts, but these bold images accent any project beautifully.

originals dies

Originals Dies

The Originals™ dies are rule-based dies measuring 4-3/4" x 5-1/2" that cut through various materials such as paper, plastic, and chipboard. Use them with Standard Cutting Pads (sold separately).

115955	Stampin' Up! Hearts & Brackets		$17.95
115971	Stampin' Up! Blossom Party		$17.95
113461	Stars #2		$15.95
114526	Circles #2		$15.95
113460	Snowflake #2		$15.95
113459	Leaves #2		$15.95
114525	Ovals		$15.95
113458	Flower Layers		$15.95
114527	Flower Layers #3		$15.95

STAMPIN' UP! HEARTS & BRACKETS

STAMPIN' UP! BLOSSOM PARTY

STARS #2

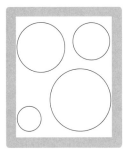

CIRCLES #2

SNOWFLAKE #2

LEAVES #2

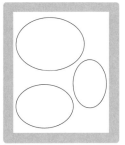

OVALS

FLOWER LAYERS

FLOWERS LAYERS #3

ORIGINALS DIES SHOWN AT 25%

STAMPIN' UP! EXCLUSIVE   CUT ——   SCORE ——   PERFORATION - - - -

albums

Use our premium, post-bound albums to store your scrapbook pages. The fabric has been pretreated with a stain-resistant coating.

albums*	linen post albums		*sm*	linen ring albums		*sm*
	12" x 12" $29.95	8-1/2" x 11" $24.95	6" x 6" $19.95	12" x 12" $26.95	8-1/2" x 11" $21.95	6" x 6" $16.95
NATURAL	104519	104520	104515	104511	104510	104509
MELLOW MOSS	105386	–	–	105393	–	105391
REAL RED	105383	–	–	105389	–	105387
NAVY	104518	–	–	104514	–	104512
*page protectors***	$10.95	$7.95	$6.95	$10.95	$7.95	$6.95
CLEAR	100670	103145	103687	104522	104523	104521

*ALL ALBUMS COME WITH 10 PAGE PROTECTORS.
**EACH PACKAGE CONTAINS 20 POLYPROPOLENE PAGE PROTECTORS.

storage

Forget-Me-Not Keeper

Use for card organization and storage. Includes 12 dividers that allow you to sort by theme, month, or occasion. 8-5/8" x 6-5/8" x 5".

105525	Forget-Me-Not Keeper*	$11.95

Ribbon Keepers

Our exclusive stackable storage boxes offer an organized way to store your ribbon. Create customized ribbon storage based on your needs. Each package includes 2 boxes, 2 divider slides, 6 connector tabs, 12 rubber feet, and instructions for assembly. The small keeper holds 3/8" ribbon. The medium keeper holds 5/8", 7/8", 1", and 1-1/4" ribbon. The large keeper holds 1/4" ribbon.

107634	Small (2)	$11.95
107635	Medium (2)	$15.95
107636	Large (2)	$18.95

Craft Keepers

Safe storage for papers, card stock, templates, and more. Velcro® closure. Expands to 1" thick.
per pkg.

104182	8-1/2" x 11" Actual size: 9" x 11-1/2"	$6.95
104181	12" x 12" Actual size: 13-1/2" x 13-1/2"	$7.95

Color Caddy

Holds 48 Classic or Craft pads and 48 refills. Rotates for easy access. Some assembly required. Pads and refills not included.

104335	Color Caddy*	$59.95

Paper Holders and Dividers

Our vertical paper holders make it easy to store and protect paper while keeping it visible and within reach. Paper holders store up to 200 sheets of card stock. Use the paper holder dividers (sold separately) to separate paper by color or pattern.

105527	Paper Holder 8-1/2" x 11"	$6.95
105526	Dividers 8-1/2" x 11" (4)	$5.25
105528	Paper Holder 12" x 12"	$7.95
105529	Dividers 12" x 12" (4)	$5.95

Color Caddy Extender Kit

The Color Caddy extender kit includes 3 stacking trays to accommodate 12 additional Stampin' Up! pads. Extender rod and assembly instructions included.

107063	Color Caddy Extender Kit	$14.95

Stampin' Stack & Store

The Stack & Store Caddy is exclusively designed to be used with our Stampin' Store containers. Stack & Store Caddy is housed on a turntable, and the containers are easily removed with one hand! Caddy holds 24 containers or 48 mini containers.

109127	Stack & Store Caddy	$34.95
103649	Stampin' Store Containers (6) 2-1/2" x 7/8"	$3.95

109689   Batty *(p. 22)* $8.50

111256   Dotted Lines *(p. 64)* $8.50

111258   Nursery Letters *(p. 76)* $8.50

105957   Bold Snowflakes* $8.50

114696   Friendly Words *(p. 100)* $8.50

113120   Santa's Lineup *(p. 41)* $8.50

115626   Bright Blessings *(p. 27)* $8.50

113632   Frightful Fence *(p. 24)* $8.50

107213   Scatter Sunshine *(p. 51)* $8.50

109686   Christmas Chatter* $8.50

112480   Haunting *(p. 22)* $8.50

116444   Sparkling *(p. 41)* $8.50

111254   Classic Stars* $8.50

116229   Hero *(p. 67)* $8.50

113832   Symphony *(p. 125)* $8.50

115624   Cornelli Lace *(p. 64)* $8.50

111201   It's Beautiful *(p. 106)* $8.50

116685   Texture *(p. 100)* $8.50

111255   Daisy Dash *(p. 65)* $8.50

106750   Kindness *(p. 51)* $8.50

109688   Whimsy *(p. 106)* $8.50

115622   Delicate Dots *(p. 65)* $8.50

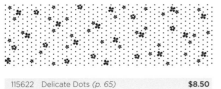

109685   Neighborhood *(p. 84)* $8.50

113834 Always in Bloom *(p. 54)* $6.50	111252 Forever Flowers *(p. 48)* $6.50	115627 Rockin' *(p. 87)* $6.50
108017 Arachnophobia *(p. 25)* $6.50	114695 Funky Forest *(p. 112)* $6.50	115121 Romance *(p. 50)* $6.50
109675 Baroque Border *(p. 131)* $6.50	115621 Hearts O' Plenty *(p. 45)* $6.50	113119 Scary Skulls *(p. 83)* $6.50
112476 Bella's Border *(p. 101)* $6.50	113831 In the Cards *(p. 121)* $6.50	113118 Skeeters *(p. 89)* $6.50
110334 Boho Friend *(p. 122)* $6.50	112479 Jolly *(p. 31)* $6.50	112968 Soft Holly *(p. 35)* $6.50
112477 Celebration *(p. 69)* $6.50	109691 Little Bits *(p. 120)* $6.50	113835 Sweet Serenity *(p. 105)* $6.50
113122 Cheers *(p. 62)* $6.50	115620 P Is for Paw *(p. 61)* $6.50	115523 Sweet Swirls *(p. 48)* $6.50
113121 Cupcakes *(p. 68)* $6.50	111251 Perfect Fit *(p. 109)* $6.50	105519 Tailgating *(p. 58)* $6.50
115625 Dream *(p. 87)* $6.50	115619 Retro Remix *(p. 114)* $6.50	104524 Time for a Tree *(p. 58)* $6.50
112478 Fall Harvest *(p. 26)* $6.50	113838 Right on Track *(p. 83)* $6.50	115666 Web *(p. 25)* $6.50
109679 Fast Flowers *(p. 56)* $6.50		

accessories index

Proprietary Rights in Trademarks and Copyrights

The contents of this catalog are protected by federal trademark and copyright registrations. Reproduction of the catalog or any portion thereof is strictly prohibited. Purchasers of Stampin' Up! products are authorized to sell hand-stamped artwork made with our copyrighted designs only in accordance with Stampin' Up!'s Angel Policy, a copy of which can be found on the Stampin' Up! Web site at www. stampinup.com, or obtained from a Stampin' Up! demonstrator. Permission is not granted to mechanically reproduce stamped images.

Ordering

All products in this catalog may be purchased only through a Stampin' Up! demonstrator. Demonstrators are independent contractors and are not employees of Stampin' Up! To help your demonstrator ensure accuracy in taking your order, always include item number, description, and price of each item ordered. Your demonstrator will provide you with two copies of your order. Please retain these copies for your personal records. You have a right to cancel order within 3 days of placing it. Ask your demonstrator for more details.

Delivery

We ship through the best carrier available. Product is usually shipped to deliver within 7 business days from the date the order is received by the company. Stampin' Up! shall not be liable for any delay in shipment that is caused in whole or in part by circumstances beyond Stampin' Up!'s control.

Guarantee

We guarantee products to be free from manufacturing defects for a period of 90 days after the shipping date. Missing items, incorrect shipments, and defective or damaged merchandise must be reported to your demonstrator within 90 days of the shipping date. This guarantee does not cover merchandise damaged through accident or misuse. If you should require assistance, please contact your demonstrator.

Exchanges & Refunds

New, unused merchandise may be exchanged at no charge within 90 days of the shipping date. The merchandise must be in the current catalog and in original shipping condition. Stamps that have been assembled cannot be exchanged. Sorry, we do not offer cash refunds. The customer is responsible for return shipping charges. If you should require assistance, please contact your demonstrator.

Limitations

Stampin' Up! reserves the right to issue a refund or substitute merchandise of similar quality and value for items that are discontinued or out of stock. The decision to discontinue merchandise and the choice of whether to issue a refund or substitution belongs solely to Stampin' Up! The items sold are craft items, and your results may vary from the examples shown. Also, actual stamps may vary somewhat in size from the images shown in this catalog, and this difference in size shall not be deemed a manufacturing defect. Information about properties of certain products (such as acid content, lignin content, and other properties affecting a product's performance or suitability for a particular use) is supplied by the product manufacturers and/or suppliers. Stampin' Up! relies on this information and does not conduct independent tests to verify the accuracy of the information supplied by product manufacturers and suppliers.

Trademark Ownership

Tombow is a registered trademark of American Tombow, Inc. Dotto, Circle Scissor Plus, Empressor, and Stamp-a-ma-jig are registered trademarks of EK Success. Glue Dots is a registered trademark of Glue Dots International. uni-ball is a registered trademark of Mitsubishi Pencil Company, Ltd. Coluzzle is a registered trademark of Provo Craft & Novelty. Watercolor Wonder is a trademark and Aqua Painter, Bold Brights, Classy Brass, Color Caddy, Color Coach, Crystal Effects, Definitely Decorative, Earth Elements, Embossing Buddy, Forget-Me-Not Keeper, Hodgepodge Hardware, In Color, Powder Pals, Rich Regals, Simply Scrappin', Simply Sent, SNAIL Adhesive, Soft Subtles, Stampin' Around, Stampin' Dimensionals, Stampin' Emboss, Stampin' Glitter, Stampin' Ink, Stampin' Kids, Stampin' Memories and the Stampin' Memories logo, Stampin' Mist, Stampin' Pad, Stampin' Pastels, Stampin' Scrub, Stampin' Up! and the Stampin' Up! box logo, Stampin' Write, Two-Step Stampin' and the 2-Step Stampin' design, The Tearing Edge, and Write Me a Memory are registered trademarks of Stampin' Up!, Inc. VersaMarker is a trademark and Encore, StäzOn, and VersaMark are registered trademarks of Tsukineko, LLC. Crop-A-Dile is a trademark of We R Memory Keepers.

Stampin' Up!
12907 South 3600 West
Riverton, UT 84065
www.stampinup.com

happy birthday

Sweet Birthday
SET OF 1 | 115564 **$7.95**

Little Boo
SET OF 1 | 115558 **$6.95**

merry & bright

Merriment
SET OF 1 | 115556 **$6.95**

welcome baby
SWEETNESS UNLIMITED

Sweetness Unlimited
SET OF 1 | 115562 **$6.95**
ESP **Dulzura sin limite** 116750
FRA **Incroyablenent mignon** 116775

Tag Tree
SET OF 1 | 115566 **$7.95**

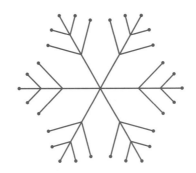

Simple Snowflake
SET OF 1 | 115554 **$7.95**

:: SIMPLY THANKS ::

thanks \ˈthaŋ(k)s\ 1 : kindly or grateful thoughts : gratitude 2 : an expression of gratitude <give *thanks* before the meal> —often used in an utterance containing no verb and serving as a courteous and somewhat informal expression of gratitude <many thanks>

Simply Thanks
SET OF 1 | 115560 **$7.95**

Dasher
SET OF 1 | 116816 **$8.95**

Ribbon of Hope
SET OF 1 | 115552 **$7.95**

Mini Note Kit
Create custom place cards in minutes with this kit. Kit includes a double-mounted stamp, 8 Very Vanilla gift cards, and a Chocolate Chip Classic Stampin' Spot.

116764 **Take Your Place** **$9.95**
Chocolate Chip, Very Vanilla

CARD: 3-7/8" x 2-3/4"

Mini Note Kit
This message on this card is simply irresistible. Kit includes a double-mounted stamp, 4 Whisper White Gift Cards & Envelopes, and a Chocolate Chip Classic Stampin' Spot.

116762 **Best of the Bunch** **$9.95**
Chocolate Chip, Whisper White

CARD: 3-7/8" x 2-3/4"
ENVELOPE: 4-1/4" x 3"

THANKS a bunch you're the best

See page 144 for the Elegant Thank You image—one more under $10 stamp.